G000168521

KS2 MATHS & ENGLISH

Ages 9-11

Written by
Paul Broadbent - Maths
Nina Filipek - English
Peter Riley - Science

Educational consultant:
Ann Dicks

Illustrated by

Rob Davis
and
Tom Connell

This edition published by Parragon in 2010

Parragon
Queen Street House
4 Queen Street
Bath BA1 1HE, UK

Copyright © Parragon Books Ltd 2009

ISBN 978-1-4454-0365-6

Printed in China

Notes to parents

The Gold Stars® key stage 2 series

The Gold Stars® Key Stage 2 series has been created to help your child revise and practise key skills and information learned in school. Each book is a complete companion to the curriculum and has been written by an expert team of teachers.

How to use this book

- Do talk about what's on the page. Let your child know that you are sharing the activities. Talking about the sections that introduce and revise essential information is particularly important. Usually children will be able to do the fill-in activities fairly independently.

- Keep work times short. Do leave a page that seems too difficult and return to it later.

- It does not matter if your child does some of the pages out of turn.

- Your child may need some extra scrap paper for working out on some of the pages.

- Check your child's answers using the answer section on pages 172-181. Give lots of praise and encouragement and remember to reward effort as well as achievement.

- Do not become anxious if your child finds any of the pages too difficult. Children learn at different rates.

Contents

Maths

Contents

Contents

Science

Decimals

Learning objective: To read whole numbers and decimals.

A decimal point separates whole numbers from decimal fractions - the parts of numbers that are less than 1.

> Decimals are often used to show the price of things.

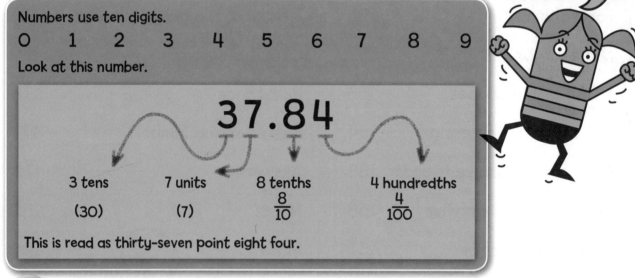

Numbers use ten digits.

0   1   2   3   4   5   6   7   8   9

Look at this number.

37.84

3 tens	7 units	8 tenths	4 hundredths
(30)	(7)	$\frac{8}{10}$	$\frac{4}{100}$

This is read as thirty-seven point eight four.

A Write the decimal number each arrow points to.

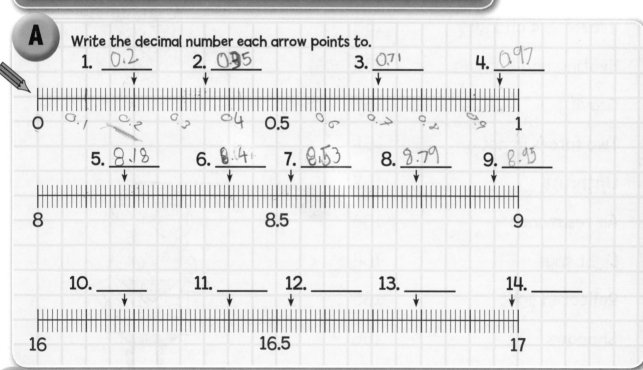

1. 0.2   2. 0.35   3. 0.71   4. 0.97

0   0.1   0.2   0.3   0.4   0.5   0.6   0.7   0.8   0.9   1

5. 8.18   6. 8.4   7. 8.53   8. 8.79   9. 8.93

8   8.5   9

10. ____ 11. ____ 12. ____ 13. ____ 14. ____

16   16.5   17

B

This table shows the weight in kilograms of some of the turtles that swim in our seas. Write the list in order of weight, starting with the heaviest.

Turtle	Weight (kilograms)	Turtle	Weight (kilograms)
Flatback turtle	78.15		
Green sea turtle	355.3		
Hawksbill turtle	62.65		
Kemp's Ridley turtle	60.45		
Leatherback turtle	462.9		
Loggerhead turtle	257.8		

C

Rearrange this set of digits to make 6 different decimal numbers between 1 and 10. Use each digit only once in each decimal number.

3　**8**　**5**　**.**

1.

_8.35_　_8.53_　_3.85_　_3.58_　_5.83_　_5.38_

2. Write the decimal numbers you have made in order, starting with the smallest.

_3.58_　_3.85_　_5.38_　_5.83_　_8.35_　_8.53_

smallest →

11

Place value

Learning objective: To use place value to multiply and divide decimals by 10.

The position of a digit in a number shows what the number is worth. This is what we mean by place value.

Making a number 10 times bigger or smaller is easy if you follow these rules:

To multiply any number by 10:
Move the digits **one place to the left**.

x10

| 3 | . | 6 | 4 |

| 3 | 6 | . | 4 | 0 |

To divide any number by 10:
Move the digits **one place to the right**.

÷10

| 1 | 4 | 8 | . | 3 |

| 1 | 4 | . | 8 | 3 |

A Answer these.

1. 1.35 x 10 = _____

2. 9.67 x 10 = _____

3. 68.5 ÷ 10 = _____

4. 334.6 ÷ 10 = _____

B Read and answer these.

1. A bucket holds 3.5 litres of water. How much water would there be in 10 buckets?

_____

2. A car travels a total of 9.85km each day. How far does the car travel after 10 days?

_____

3. A 250kg sack of grain is divided into 10 packs. How much does each pack of grain weigh?

_____

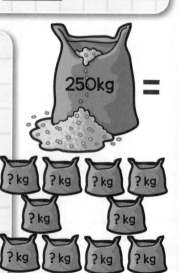

250kg =

? kg   ? kg   ? kg   ? kg
  ? kg   ? kg
? kg   ? kg   ? kg   ? kg

This is a **super-square**:

x10 →

7	70	700
0.7	7	70
0.07	0.7	7

÷10 ↓

Putting a zero on the end of a decimal number does not change the number. 3.8 is the same as 3.80!

C Complete these **super-squares**.

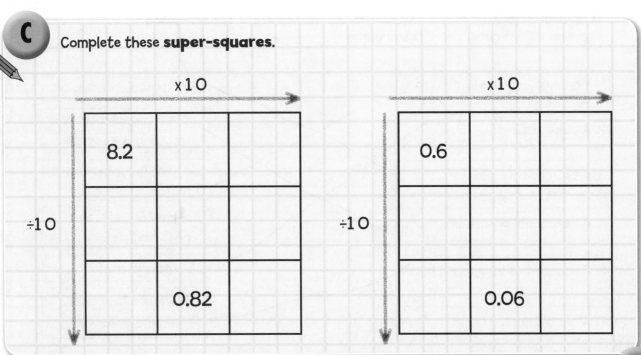

x10 →

8.2		
	0.82	

÷10 ↓

x10 →

0.6		
	0.06	

÷10 ↓

3D shapes

Learning objective: To describe the properties of 3D shapes.

A solid shape has three dimensions: height, length and width.

> **What shape are cereal boxes?**

Solid or 3D shapes are made up of **faces**, **edges** and **vertices** (corners).

A cuboid has 6 faces, 12 edges and 8 vertices.

An edge is where two faces meet.

A face is a flat surface of a solid.

Vertex is another word for corner. The plural is vertices.

A   Match each description to the shape name to complete the sentences.

triangular prism   cube   tetrahedron   hexagonal prism   square-based pyramid   cuboid

1. A triangular prism has...	...4 triangular faces.
2. A cube has...	...2 hexagonal faces and 6 rectangular faces.
3. A tetrahedron has...	...2 triangular faces and 3 rectangular faces.
4. A hexagonal prism has...	...6 rectangular faces and 2 square faces.
5. A square-based pyramid has...	...6 square faces.
6. A cuboid has...	...1 square face and 4 triangular faces.

Prisms

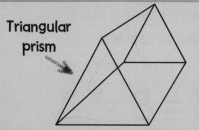

Triangular
prism

Prisms have rectangular faces, with
the shape of the end face giving each
prism its name.

Cuboids and **cubes** are special types
of prism.

Pyramids

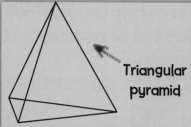

Triangular
pyramid

The shape of the base gives each
pyramid its name. The triangular faces
of a pyramid all meet at a point.

Another name for a triangular pyramid is
a **tetrahedron**.

B Sort these shapes into prisms and pyramids. Complete the table below.

A

B

C

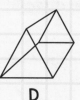

D

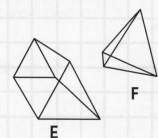

E

F

G

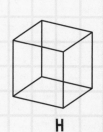

H

	A	B	C	D	E	F	G	H
Prism	✔	✔	✔	✔	✔		✔	
Pyramid						✔	✔	

Mental calculation

Learning objective: To be able to calculate mentally and use brackets.

Subtraction is the inverse or opposite of addition.
Division is the inverse or opposite of multiplication.
Use these facts to help you work out calculations with missing numbers.
Missing numbers can be represented by boxes, shapes or letters.

Knowing your multiplication tables and addition bonds is important.

_____ $\div 5 = 8$

Use multiplication:

$8 \times 5 =$ _____ → $8 \times 5 = 40$ → So $40 \div 5 = 8$

When part of a problem is in brackets, you work out the bracket part first.

$15 - (8 + 4) =$ _____ $(15 - 8) + 4 =$ _____

$15 - 12 = 3$ $7 + 4 = 11$

A Write the missing number to complete these calculations.

1. 25 + __6__ = 31

2. _16_ (- 9) = 7 +9

3. 17 + _7_ = 24

4. _18_ (- 13) = 5 +13

5. 14 + _____ = 23

6. _____ ÷ 6 = 2

7. 45 ÷ _____ = 9

8. 4 x _____ = 24

9. _____ x 3 = 21

10. _____ ÷ 9 = 7

11. _____ x 6 = 54

12. 7 x _____ = 42

DEFINITION

inverse The opposite, for example, forwards is the inverse of backwards and in maths, adding is the inverse of taking away.

B Write the answer for each of these.
Remember to work the brackets out first.

1. $(19 - 3) + 4 =$ _____

2. $14 - (7 + 2) =$ _____

3. $(13 - 5) \times 2 =$ _____

4. $16 - (8 - 3) =$ _____

5. $3 \times (9 - 5) =$ _____

6. $(4 + 6) \div 2 =$ _____

7. $(8 + 2) - (3 + 5) =$ _____

8. $(9 \times 3) + (4 \times 5) =$ _____

C Draw brackets to make each answer 12.

1. 19 - 12 - 5

2. 16 - 10 - 6

3. 22 - 5 + 5

4. 6 + 13 - 7

5. 24 - 6 - 6

6. 20 - 10 - 2

Try using opposite calculations to find the number.

D What's my number?
Work out the mystery number for each of these.

1. When I divide my number by 6 the answer is 8.   64

2. When I multiply my number by 6 the answer is 42.   72

3. When I double my number and then add 3 the answer is 19.   19

4. When I divide my number by 3 and then add 5 the answer is 12.   12

5. When I multiply my number by 5 and then subtract 6 the answer is 39.   9

6. When I divide my number by 4 and then subtract 2 the answer is 3.   6

Make up your own mystery number puzzles like this.

Square numbers

Learning objective: To know the squares of numbers up to 10 x 10.

When two identical whole numbers are multiplied together they make a
square number.

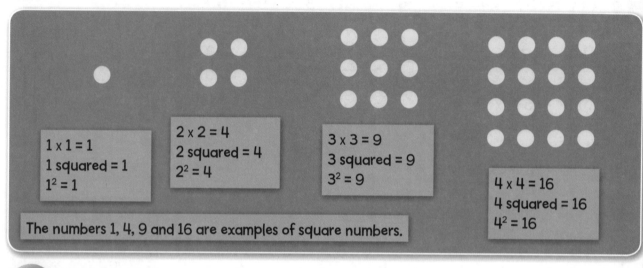

1 x 1 = 1
1 squared = 1
$1^2 = 1$

2 x 2 = 4
2 squared = 4
$2^2 = 4$

3 x 3 = 9
3 squared = 9
$3^2 = 9$

4 x 4 = 16
4 squared = 16
$4^2 = 16$

The numbers 1, 4, 9 and 16 are examples of square numbers.

A Write the missing numbers to complete this multiplication table.

	0	1	2	3	4	5	6	7	8	9	10
0	0	0		0	0			0	0		0
1		1	2			5	6	7		9	10
2	0		4	6	8				16	18	
3		3		9	12		18	21			
4	0				16				32		
5				15	20	25	30			45	
6							36				
7	0	7						49			
8		8		24		40		56	64	72	
9	0									81	
10		10			40				80		100

B Colour the square for each of these in the multiplication table opposite.

1 x 1 2 x 2 3 x 3 4 x 4 5 x 5 6 x 6 7 x 7 8 x 8 9 x 9 10 x 10

What do you notice?

C Circle the numbers in each set that are **not** square numbers.

1. 36   24   16   64   48

2. 25   81   9   15   12

3. 1   100 46   4   49

4. 18   49   9   81   77

5. 36   6   4   64   50

6. 49   9   39   100 92

Read across and down to multiply 2 numbers together. If you go across from 5 and down from 4 it meets at 20. So 5 x 4 = 20 and 4 x 5 = 20!

D Answer these.

1. $4^2 =$ _____
2. $7^2 =$ _____
3. $6^2 =$ _____
4. $9^2 =$ _____
5. $1^2 =$ _____
6. $2^2 =$ _____
7. $10^2 =$ _____
8. $3^2 =$ _____
9. $8^2 =$ _____
10. $5^2 =$ _____

Multiples and factors

Learning objective: To identify pairs of factors and find common multiples.

A **multiple** of a whole number is produced by multiplying that number by another whole number. **Factors** of a number can divide that number exactly.

Multiples of 3 →	3	6	9		15	18...	60...	300...
Multiples of 4 →	4	8		16	20	24...	80...	400...

12 is a multiple of both 3 and 4.
This means that 12 is a **common multiple** of 3 and 4.

Factors divide a number exactly.

10 has 4 factors because it can only be divided exactly by 4 numbers.

Factors of 10 in order: 1, 2, 5, 10
Factors of 10 in pairs: (1, 10) (2, 5)

$10 \div 1 = 10$
$10 \div 2 = 5$
$10 \div 5 = 2$
$10 \div 10 = 1$

A Write all the pairs of factors for each of these numbers.

1. 8
    (__,__) (__,__)

2. 20
    (__,__) (__,__)

    (__,__)

3. 24
    (__,__) (__,__)

    (__,__) (__,__)

4. 28
    (__,__) (__,__)

    (__,__)

DEFINITION

multiple A multiple is a number made by multiplying together two other numbers.

B

Write the first 10 multiples for each of these numbers.

1. multiples of 4 → ___ ___ ___ ___ ___ ___ ___ ___ ___ ___
2. multiples of 3 → ___ ___ ___ ___ ___ ___ ___ ___ ___ ___
3. multiples of 6 → ___ ___ ___ ___ ___ ___ ___ ___ ___ ___
4. multiples of 5 → ___ ___ ___ ___ ___ ___ ___ ___ ___ ___
5. multiples of 10 → ___ ___ ___ ___ ___ ___ ___ ___ ___ ___
6. multiples of 8 → ___ ___ ___ ___ ___ ___ ___ ___ ___ ___

C

Look at your answers for Exercise B. Use the list of multiples to help you find the common multiples for each of these pairs of numbers.

1. 3 and 5 → _____ _____
2. 4 and 3 → _____ _____
3. 4 and 5 → _____ _____

4. 6 and 8 → _____ _____
5. 10 and 6 → _____ _____
6. 6 and 4 → _____ _____ _____

D

Write these numbers in the correct part of the Venn diagram.

12   4   18
10   24   16
15   3   20
9   6   25
2   30   1

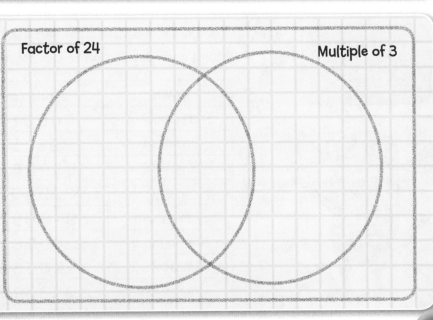

Factor of 24   Multiple of 3

Rounding numbers

Learning objective: To use rounding and approximation to estimate calculations.

We round numbers to make them easier to work with. It is useful for estimating approximate, or rough, answers.

Whole numbers can be rounded to the nearest 10, 100 or 1000. Decimal numbers can be rounded to the nearest whole number or tenth.

To round large numbers to the nearest 100:

Look at the **tens** digit.

Round down if the digit is less than 5 (value less than 50).

Round up if the digit is 5 or more.

68428 round down to 68400
304659 round up to 305700

To round decimals to the nearest whole number:

Look at the $\frac{1}{10}$ (tenth) digit.

Round down if the digit is less than 5 (value less than 0.5).

Round up if the digit is 5 or more.

4.47 round down to 4
12.75 round up to 13

Tip: focus on the last 3 digits in each number.

A This chart shows some cities with a population of less than 1 million. Round each population to the nearest 100.

Town	Population	Nearest 100
Liverpool	469019	
Bradford	293717	
Sheffield	439866	
Derby	229407	
Birmingham	970892	
Nottingham	249584	
Bristol	420556	
Plymouth	243795	

B

Round each number to the nearest 100, then do the sum.

1. 415 + 388 → _____
2. 682 - 174 → _____
3. 597 - 489 → _____
4. 378 + 836 → _____
5. 2190 + 3675 → _____
6. 9251 + 4359 → _____

C

Round each of these to the nearest whole number of kilograms. Write the approximate total weights for each set.

1.	4.38 kg	2.97 kg	9.19 kg	Approx. total weight _____ kg
2.	9.49 kg	7.73 kg	3.64 kg	Approx. total weight _____ kg
3.	13.85 kg	12.55 kg	6.53 kg	Approx. total weight _____ kg
4.	19.09 kg	17.64 kg	8.47 kg	Approx. total weight _____ kg

D

Calculators can display lots of decimal places. We often round off numbers to 2 decimal places.

0.76398 → rounds down to 0.76

3.42739 → rounds up to 3.43

Round these to 2 decimal places.

1. 0.9286 _____
2. 7.0835 _____
3. 12.945 _____
4. 7.5881 _____
5. 2.9116 _____
6. 30.0794 _____

23

Measuring length

Learning objective: To convert units of length and measure lines accurately.

We measure **length** using kilometres, metres, centimetres and millimetres.

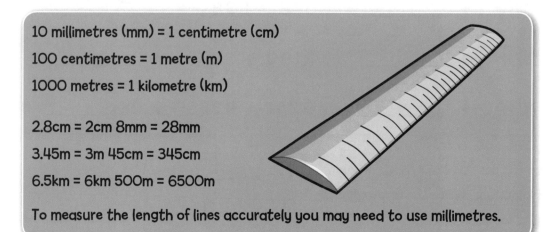

10 millimetres (mm) = 1 centimetre (cm)

100 centimetres = 1 metre (m)

1000 metres = 1 kilometre (km)

2.8cm = 2cm 8mm = 28mm

3.45m = 3m 45cm = 345cm

6.5km = 6km 500m = 6500m

To measure the length of lines accurately you may need to use millimetres.

A   Complete these.

1. 58 mm = _____ cm

2. 10.67 m = _____ cm

3. 910 cm = _____ m

4. 13.5 cm = _____ mm

5. 8.3 km = _____ m

6. 94 mm = _____ cm

7. 3700 m = _____ km

8. 14.6 cm = _____ mm

Your work on decimals on page 10 will help you with these conversions.

DEFINITION

cm means centimetre.
m means metre.
km means kilometre.

B Use a ruler to measure the length of each line accurately in millimetres.

1. _____

2. _____

3. _____

4. _____

5. _____

6. _____

C The perimeter of a shape is the distance all around the edge. These shapes are all regular, so each side is the same length.

Measure the length of one side of each shape in millimetres. Use this measurement to work out the perimeter of each shape.

1. = _____ mm

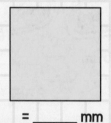

2. = _____ mm

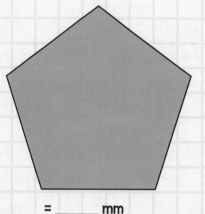

3. = _____ mm

4.

= _____ mm

> Use millimetres when you need to measure something accurately.

24-hour clock

Timetables and digital watches often use the 24-hour clock.

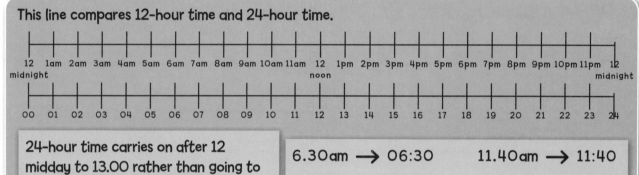

This line compares 12-hour time and 24-hour time.

| 12 midnight | 1am | 2am | 3am | 4am | 5am | 6am | 7am | 8am | 9am | 10am | 11am | 12 noon | 1pm | 2pm | 3pm | 4pm | 5pm | 6pm | 7pm | 8pm | 9pm | 10pm | 11pm | 12 midnight |

| 00 | 01 | 02 | 03 | 04 | 05 | 06 | 07 | 08 | 09 | 10 | 11 | 12 | 13 | 14 | 15 | 16 | 17 | 18 | 19 | 20 | 21 | 22 | 23 | 24 |

24-hour time carries on after 12 midday to 13.00 rather than going to 1.00pm. For afternoon and evening times just add 12 to each time to change from 12-hour to 24-hour time.

6.30 am → 06:30   11.40 am → 11:40
6.30 pm → 18:30   11.40 pm → 23:40

A Write these times as 24-hour clock times.

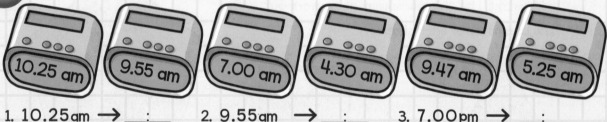

10.25 am   9.55 am   7.00 am   4.30 am   9.47 am   5.25 am

1. 10.25 am → __:__   2. 9.55 am → __:__   3. 7.00 pm → __:__
4. 4.30 pm → __:__   5. 9.47 am → __:__   6. 5.25 pm → __:__

B Write these times as 12-hour clock times, using am and pm.

13:50   11:08   09:22   23:10   15:59   21:24

1. 13:50 → __.__   2. 11:08 → __.__   3. 09:22 → __.__
4. 23:10 → __.__   5. 15:59 → __.__   6. 21:34 → __.__

DEFINITION

am 'Ante meridiem' meaning 'before midday'.

pm 'Post meridiem' meaning 'after midday'.

C

Write these same times in two lists, showing the times as both 24-hour and 12-hour times.

07:00

11.35am

Event	12-hour time	24-hour time
Alarm wake up	7.00am	07:00

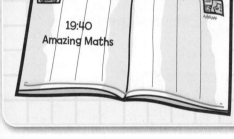

19:40 Amazing Maths

taxi 7.15pm

14:18

Meet for coffee 10.00am

D

6th July, 1989 at 11.45pm was a very special time.

It could be written as:

23:45 6.7.89!

What will be special about 8.10pm on 20th October 2010?

_____

Work out some other special dates and times.

Find out about the date and time when you were born!

Equivalents

Learning objective: To find equivalent percentages, decimals and fractions.

Percentages are fractions out of 100.

'per cent' means 'out of 100' and % is the percentage sign.

Look at this grid.
25% of the grid is red.

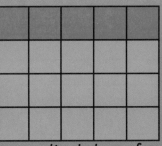

$$\frac{5}{20} = \frac{25}{100} = 25\%$$

25% is the same as $\frac{1}{4}$.

Look at these methods for converting between fractions, percentages and decimals:

Per cent to decimal

Divide the percentage by 100

Example: 60% is the same as 0.6

Decimal to per cent

Multiply the decimal by 100

Example: 0.25 is the same as 25%

Per cent to fraction

Write the percentage as a fraction out of 100 and then simplify

Example: 40% is $\frac{40}{100}$, which is the same as $\frac{2}{5}$

Fraction to per cent

Write the fraction as a decimal and then multiply by 100

Example: $\frac{3}{4}$ is 0.75 which is the same as 75%

A Use the methods shown above to change these fractions and decimals to percentages.

Turn to page 6 for revision on decimals.

1. $\frac{3}{10}$ ____   2. $\frac{1}{5}$ ____   3. $\frac{7}{100}$ ____   4. $\frac{11}{50}$ ____

5. 0.8 ____   6. 0.1 ____   7. 0.65 ____   8. 0.12 ____

DEFINITION

equivalent A number or an amount that is equal or the same.

B Write the missing digits to complete these.

1. $\frac{1}{2}$ = 0._____ = 50%

2. $\frac{1}{4}$ = 0.25 = _____%

3. $\frac{1}{20}$ = 0.05 = _____%

4. $\frac{2}{\boxed{}}$ = 0.4 = 40%

5. $\frac{17}{50}$ = 0._____ = 34%

6. $\frac{7}{10}$ = 0.7 = _____%

C Write the fraction and percentage shown by the shaded part of each shape.

1.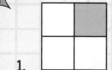

2.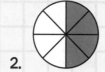

3.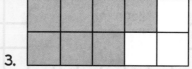

4.

5.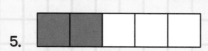

6.

D Write the percentages for each of these headlines.

1. There was a one-in-a-hundred chance of finding the treasure.

   There was a _____% chance of finding the treasure.

2. Eight out of ten children like maths more than any other subject.

   _____% of children like maths more than any other subject.

3. Four in five people read our newspaper!

   _____% of people read our newspaper!

   The rest look at the pictures. . .

4. Our football team won sixteen of their last twenty matches.

   Our football team won _____% of their last twenty matches.

Measures

Learning objective: To use standard units of measure and convert between units.

As well as measuring length, we can measure weight (mass) and volume (capacity).

Measuring mass

Mass (or weight) is a measure of how heavy an object is.

Metric units of mass are **kilograms (kg)** and **grams (g).**

There are 1000g in 1kg.

1000 grams = 1 kilogram
2400g = 2.4kg

Measuring capacity

Capacity is about how much something holds.

Metric units of capacity are **litres (l)** and **millilitres (ml).**

There are 1000ml in 1l.

1000 millilitres = 1 litre
1800ml = 1.8l

A Write the mass shown on each set of scales in grams and kilograms.

1.  500g _____ g = _____ kg

2.  800g _____ g = _____ kg

3.  1400g _____ g = _____ kg

4.  1900g _____ g = _____ kg

5.  2000g _____ g = _____ kg

DEFINITION

kg means kilogram.

g means gram.

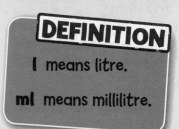

DEFINITION

l means litre.

ml means millilitre.

B Write the amount of water in each jug both as millilitres and litres.

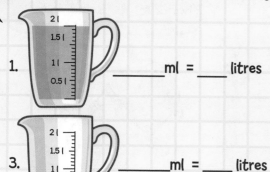

1. _____ ml = _____ litres

2. _____ ml = _____ litres

3. _____ ml = _____ litres

4. _____ ml = _____ litres

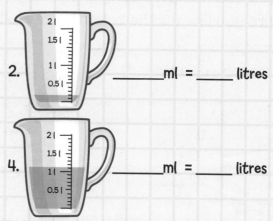

C Circle the greater amount in each pair.

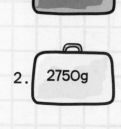

1. 4kg   4g

2. 2750g   2.5kg

3. 550g   5.5kg

4. 3kg   2999g

5. 100ml   1 litre

6. 6500ml   5.6 litres

7. 1.2 litres   120ml

8. 4000ml   0.4 litres

Written addition

When you add numbers using this written method, make sure you line up the columns carefully.

The columns are: thousands, hundreds, tens and units.

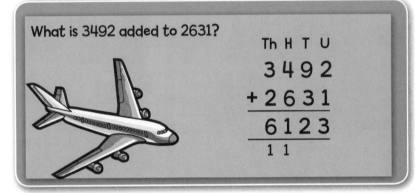

What is 3492 added to 2631?

```
  Th H T U
    3 4 9 2
  + 2 6 3 1
    6 1 2 3
      1 1
```

Look out for addition words in problems: add, total, sum, altogether, greater than...

A Answer these.

1. 6728
   +2740

2. 3128
   +4675

3. 1561
   +2918

4. 4870
   +4693

5. 3667
   +3843

6. 2035
   +1985

B Read and answer these. Use a pen and paper to work out each calculation.

1. Add together 3945 and 5680. _____

2. What is 5929 and 3874 added together? _____

3. What is the sum of 2263 and 3815? _____

4. Total 5923 and 1946. _____

5. What is the total of 4328 and 2749? _____

6. What number is 4444 greater than 1991? _____

DEFINITION

addition Finding the total of two or more numbers. The + sign shows that numbers are being added together.

C

Look at these distances and work out the different totals.

A → 1652km   B → 3559km   C → 3081km   D → 2722 km   E → 1768km

1. A + E   →   _____ km

4. C + E   →   _____ km

2. D + C   →   _____ km

5. E + D   →   _____ km

3. B + D   →   _____ km

D

All the digits 1 and 3 are missing.

Write the digits 1 or 3 in the correct place to complete this addition.

```
    4  6  □  8
+      9  □  6  □
  _____
  □  □  8  0  □
```

Use your knowledge of place value.

Write the numbers 1 and 3 on six small pieces of paper and try them in the different missing boxes to see which ones work.

Written subtraction

Learning objective: To use efficient written methods to subtract whole numbers.

There are different ways of taking one number away from another.
If you can't work it out in your head you can try written methods.

Example
What is 3674 subtract 1738?

Step 1

Rename 70 + 4 as 60 + 14

14 - 8 = 6

```
    3 6 ⁶7 ¹4
  - 1 7 3 8
            6
```

Step 2

60 - 30 = 30

```
    3 6 ⁶7 ¹4
  - 1 7 3 8
          3 6
```

Make sure you line up the columns correctly.

Step 3

Rename 3000 + 600 as 2000 + 1600.

1600 - 700 = 900

```
    ²3̶ ¹6 ⁶7 ¹4
  - 1 7 3 8
        9 3 6
```

Step 4

2000 - 1000 = 1000

```
    ²3̶ ¹6 ⁶7 ¹4
  - 1 7 3 8
      1 9 3 6
```

A

Write the answers.

1. 4738
   -1592

2. 9471
   -3803

3. 6545
   -2175

4. 5962-4689

5. 7712-2935

6. 7348-2689

B

Write the missing digits in these subtractions.

1.
```
   3  8  4  ☐
-  1  7  ☐  2
───────────────
   2  ☐  8  5
```

2.
```
   7  ☐  4  3
-  2  4  8  ☐
───────────────
   ☐  4  5  7
```

3.
```
   4  1  1  5
-  2  ☐  3  ☐
───────────────
   ☐  1  7  9
```

C

This table shows the depths of the deepest oceans and seas in the world.
Look at the table and answer the questions.

Ocean/sea	Average depth (metres)
Pacific Ocean	4028 m
Indian Ocean	3963 m
Atlantic Ocean	3926 m
Caribbean Sea	2647 m
South China Sea	1652 m
Bering Sea	1547 m
Gulf of Mexico	1486 m
Mediterranean Sea	1429 m

1. How much deeper is the Caribbean Sea than the Gulf of Mexico?

2. By how many metres is the Pacific Ocean deeper than the Caribbean Sea?

3. What is the difference in depth between the Atlantic Ocean and the Caribbean Sea?

4. Which two seas have a difference in depth of 1100m?

5. Which sea is 1316m less in depth than the Indian Ocean?

6. Which two oceans or seas have the smallest difference in depth?

Angles

Learning objective: To measure and calculate angles in straight lines and triangles.

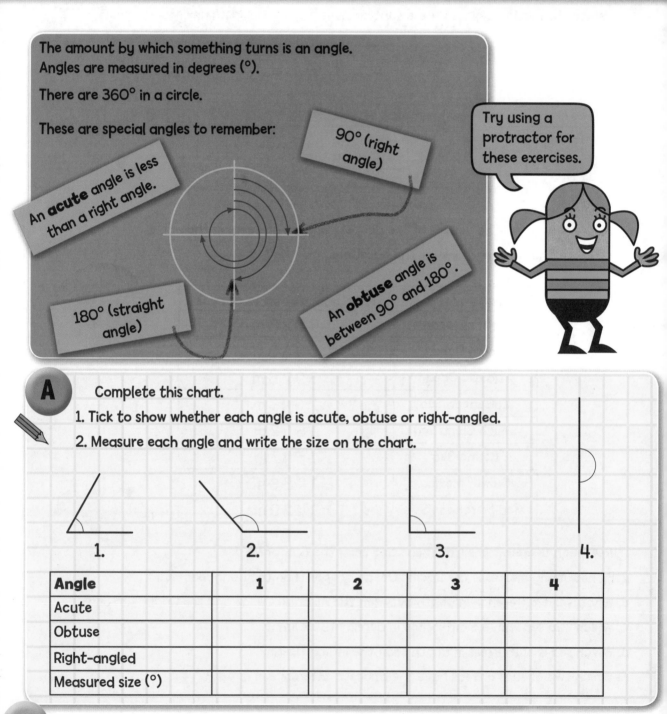

The amount by which something turns is an angle.
Angles are measured in degrees (°).

There are 360° in a circle.

These are special angles to remember:

90° (right angle)

An **acute** angle is less than a right angle.

180° (straight angle)

An **obtuse** angle is between 90° and 180°.

Try using a protractor for these exercises.

A Complete this chart.

1. Tick to show whether each angle is acute, obtuse or right-angled.
2. Measure each angle and write the size on the chart.

1.   2.   3.   4.

Angle	1	2	3	4
Acute				
Obtuse				
Right-angled				
Measured size (°)				

B Write the missing angle on each of these shapes.

1. 69° 68°

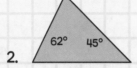

2. 62° 45°

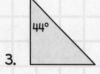

3. 44°

C Write the missing angle for each of these.

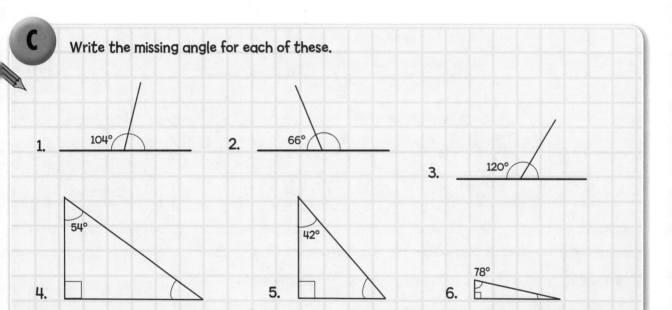

1. 104°

2. 66°

3. 120°

4. 54°

5. 42°

6. 78°

D Write the two missing angles on these.

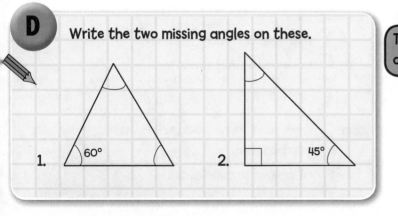

1. 60°

2. 45°

The angles of a triangle add up to 180 degrees.

37

2D shapes

Learning objective: To describe the properties of polygons.

Polygons are straight-sided, closed shapes. Quadrilaterals are any shapes with 4 straight sides.

Learn the properties of these different polygons:

Number of sides		Name	Number of sides		Name
3		Triangle	6		Hexagon
4		Quadrilateral	7		Heptagon
5		Pentagon	8		Octagon

Learn the properties of these different quadrilaterals:

Square
- 4 equal sides
- 4 right angles

Rectangle
- 2 pairs of equal sides
- 4 right angles

Rhombus
- 4 equal sides
- opposite angles equal
- opposite sides parallel

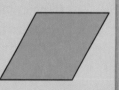

Parallelogram
- opposite sides are equal and parallel

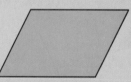

Kite
- 2 pairs of adjacent sides that are equal

Trapezium
- 1 pair of parallel sides

A Count the sides and write the name for each shape.

1. _____

2. _____

3. _____

4. _____

5. _____

6. _____

B Name each of these quadrilaterals.

1. _____

2. _____

3. _____

4. _____

5. _____

6. _____

C Complete these sentences by writing <u>always</u>, <u>sometimes</u> or <u>never</u>.

Look at the shapes on these two pages to help you.

1. A rectangle _____ has 4 right angles.

2. An octagon _____ has 7 sides.

3. A square is _____ symmetrical.

4. A parallelogram is _____ symmetrical.

5. A triangle _____ has a right angle.

6. A rhombus _____ has all sides the same length.

Moving shapes

Learning objective: To draw shapes on grids after translation, reflection or rotation.

A shape can be moved by translation, reflection or rotation.

Translation: sliding a shape without rotating or flipping over.

This shape has moved 4 squares across and 1 square down.

Reflection: this is sometimes called a 'flip'.

Rotation: a shape can be rotated around a point, clockwise or anti-clockwise.

Shape A is rotated clockwise around point X to become shape B.

Point X

A Write whether these shapes have been **translated**, **rotated** or **reflected**.

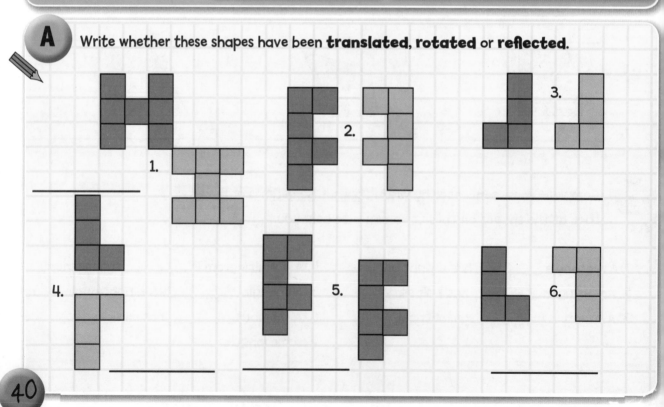

1. _____

2. _____

3. _____

4. _____

5. _____

6. _____

DEFINITION

clockwise Moving in the same direction as the hands of a clock.

B Repeat these shape tiles to design a larger pattern.

Decide whether to rotate, reflect or translate each tile.

Can you make a symmetrical pattern?

C Copy this tile and repeat it 10 times.

Use it to make a pattern of translated, rotated or reflected tiles.

Design your own tile and explore the patterns you can make.

DEFINITION

anti-clockwise Moving in the opposite direction to the hands of a clock.

41

Written multiplication

Learning objective: To use written methods to multiply TU (tens and units) x TU.

When you need to multiply two numbers together, decide whether you are able to work out the answer in your head, or whether you need to use a written method.

Look at these two written methods for 34 x 26:

Method 1

x	30	4
20	600	80
6	180	24

600 | 80 → 680
180 | 24 → + 204
884

Method 2

```
      34
    x 26
     204   (34 x 6)
     680   (34 x 20)
     884
```

It is always a good idea to estimate the answer first and then check your final answer with your estimate.

A Complete these multiplications.

1. 19 x 76 = _____

2. 84 x 37 = _____

3.
```
    1 9
  x 2 4
  _____

  _____
```

4.
```
    5 3
  x 6 2
  _____

  _____
```

B

Read and answer these.

1. There are 24 hours in a day. How many hours are there in September?
2. A truck makes a 58-km journey 16 times in a week. How far did the truck travel in total?
3. A packet of nuts weighs 28g and there are 25 packets in box. How many grams of nuts are there in a full box?
4. A recipe makes 24 cakes, each weighing 75g. What is the total weight of ingredients in this recipe?
5. A roll of wire is 18m in length. How much wire will there be in 35 rolls?
6. There are 15 pencils in a pack and a school orders 49 packs. How many pencils will there be altogether?

C

This is an order form for equipment for a school.

Write how many of each item has been ordered.

Items	Amount in 1 pack	Number of packs	Total number of items
Pencils	28	76	
Chalk	15	33	
Sharpeners	26	19	
Erasers	48	14	
Pens	52	58	
Crayons	34	47	

D

Write the digits 3, 4, 5 and 6 on small pieces of paper.

Arrange them to make different multiplications.

 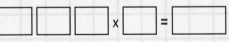

What is the largest answer you can make?
What is the smallest answer?
What answer is the nearest you can make to 1000?

43

Written division

Some dividing you can do in your head as it links with multiplying. 48 divided by 6 is 8, which is easy if you know that 6 x 8 is 48. When you divide bigger numbers, you need to use a written method.

Remember!
If a number cannot be divided exactly it leaves a remainder.

What is 749 divided by 4?

Work out how many groups of 4 are in 749 and what is left over:

Method 1

```
      187 r1
  4)749
   -400      (4 x 100)
    349
   -320      (4 x 80)
     29
    -28      (4 x 7)      749 ÷ 4 = 187 remainder 1
      1
```

Method 2

```
      187 r1
  4)7³4 ²9
```

A Complete these divisions and write the answers with remainders.

1. 488 ÷ 3 → _____ r __
   3)488

2. 367 ÷ 5 → _____ r __
   5)367

3. 189 ÷ 4 → _____ r __
   4)1 8 9

4. 926 ÷ 4 → _____ r __
   4)926

DEFINITION

remainder If a number cannot be divided exactly by another number then there is a whole number answer with an amount left over, called a remainder.

B

Draw a line to match each remainder to a division.

271 ÷ 6

315 ÷ 8

454 ÷ 5

608 ÷ 3

Remainder
1
2
3
4
5
6
7
8
9

149 ÷ 6

259 ÷ 9

359 ÷ 10

458 ÷ 9

398 ÷ 7

Use paper for written workings out.

C

Eggs are collected every day and put into boxes of 6. Write how many full boxes can be made each day and how many eggs are left over to complete this chart.

Day of the week	Eggs collected	Number of	
		Full boxes (6 eggs)	**Eggs left over**
Monday	627		
Tuesday	572		
Wednesday	700		
Thursday	644		
Friday	683		
Saturday	594		
Sunday	735		

Area

Learning objective: To be able to calculate the area of shapes.

The area of a shape is the amount of surface that it covers.

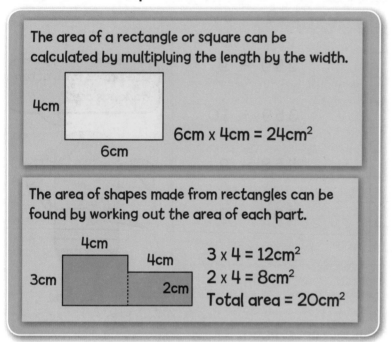

The area of a rectangle or square can be calculated by multiplying the length by the width.

4cm

6cm

6cm x 4cm = 24cm²

The area of shapes made from rectangles can be found by working out the area of each part.

4cm

4cm

3cm

2cm

3 x 4 = 12cm²
2 x 4 = 8cm²
Total area = 20cm²

Area is measured in square units, such as square centimetres (cm²) and square metres (m²).

A Calculate the area of each of these.

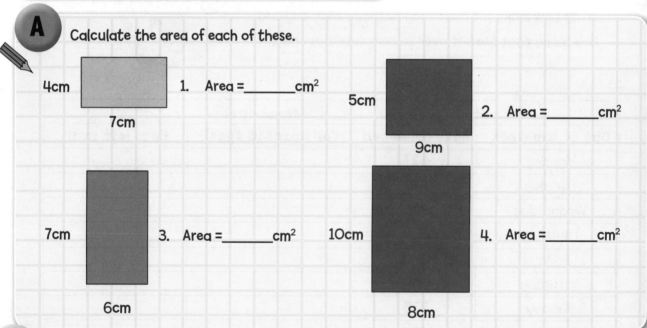

4cm

7cm

1.   Area =_____cm²

5cm

9cm

2.   Area =_____cm²

7cm

6cm

3.   Area =_____cm²

10cm

8cm

4.   Area =_____cm²

Remember!
These shapes below are
not drawn to actual size.

B Write the area for each of these shapes.

6cm

1. Area =_____cm²

2cm

5cm

2. Area =_____cm²

3cm

4cm

3. Area =_____cm²

5cm

4. Area =_____cm²

4cm

3cm

C Calculate the area of these shapes. Work out the area of each rectangle within the shape first.

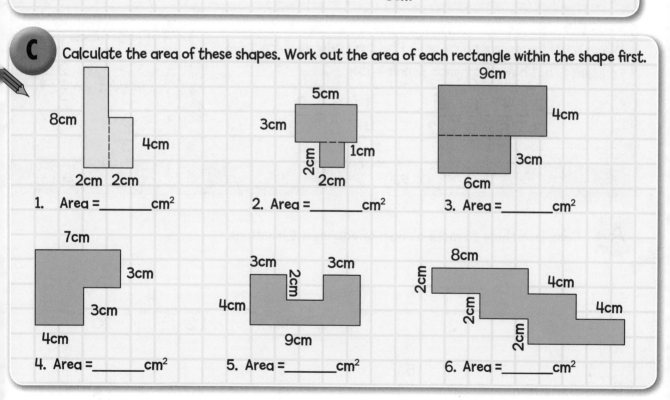

9cm

5cm

8cm

3cm

4cm

4cm

1cm

2cm

2cm 2cm

2cm

6cm

3cm

1. Area =_____cm²

2. Area =_____cm²

3. Area =_____cm²

7cm

3cm

3cm 3cm

8cm

2cm

3cm

2cm

4cm

4cm

4cm

2cm

2cm

4cm

9cm

4. Area =_____cm²

5. Area =_____cm²

6. Area =_____cm²

47

Comparing fractions

Learning objective: To know how to compare and order a set of fractions.

You may need to work out which fraction is bigger when you are comparing amounts.

For example, which would give you more of a cake: $\frac{2}{3}$ of it, or $\frac{3}{4}$ of the cake? This is tricky with different denominators.

Comparing fractions with the same denominator is easy:
For example, $\frac{4}{5}$ is bigger than $\frac{2}{5}$

$\frac{4}{5}$

$\frac{2}{5}$

To compare any fractions change them to equivalent fractions with a **common denominator**. This means they have the same denominator.

Example
Which is the larger fraction: $\frac{2}{3}$ or $\frac{3}{4}$? Find the equivalent fractions to $\frac{2}{3}$ and $\frac{3}{4}$ that have a common denominator.

$$\frac{2}{3} = \frac{4}{6} = \frac{6}{9} = \frac{\mathbf{8}}{\mathbf{12}} \qquad \frac{3}{4} = \frac{6}{8} = \frac{\mathbf{9}}{\mathbf{12}}$$

$\frac{9}{12}$ is larger than $\frac{8}{12}$

$\frac{3}{4}$ is larger than $\frac{2}{3}$

$\frac{3}{4} > \frac{2}{3}$

A Complete these to make a chain of equivalent fractions.

1. $\dfrac{1}{3} = \dfrac{\square}{6} = \dfrac{3}{\square} = \dfrac{5}{12} ... $

1. $\dfrac{1}{3} = \dfrac{\square}{6} = \dfrac{3}{\square} = \dfrac{\square}{12} = \dfrac{5}{\square} = \dfrac{\square}{\square}$

2. $\dfrac{1}{4} = \dfrac{2}{\square} = \dfrac{\square}{12} = \dfrac{4}{\square} = \dfrac{\square}{20} = \dfrac{\square}{\square}$

3. $\dfrac{1}{2} = \dfrac{\square}{4} = \dfrac{3}{\square} = \dfrac{\square}{8} = \dfrac{5}{\square} = \dfrac{\square}{\square}$

4. $\dfrac{2}{3} = \dfrac{4}{\square} = \dfrac{\square}{9} = \dfrac{8}{\square} = \dfrac{\square}{15} = \dfrac{\square}{\square}$

DEFINITION

denominator The bottom number of a fraction.
Example: $\frac{2}{3}$

B

Write < or > or = between each pair of fractions.

Use your completed equivalent fractions chains from Exercise A to help you change them to equivalent fractions.

1. $\frac{2}{3}$ $\frac{1}{2}$

2. $\frac{1}{4}$ $\frac{1}{3}$

3. $\frac{2}{3}$ $\frac{4}{5}$

4. $\frac{1}{2}$ $\frac{3}{4}$

5. $\frac{4}{5}$ $\frac{1}{2}$

6. $\frac{1}{2}$ $\frac{1}{3}$

7. $\frac{3}{4}$ $\frac{4}{5}$

8. $\frac{4}{5}$ $\frac{1}{3}$

< means less than.
> means more than.

C

Draw a line and join each of these fractions to its correct place on this number line.

0 ———————————— 1

$\frac{1}{10}$ $\frac{3}{4}$ $\frac{9}{10}$ $\frac{2}{5}$ $\frac{1}{5}$ $\frac{7}{10}$ $\frac{6}{10}$ $\frac{1}{2}$ $\frac{3}{5}$ $\frac{1}{4}$ $\frac{3}{10}$ $\frac{4}{5}$

D

Put each group of fractions in order starting with the smallest.

1. $\frac{1}{4}$ $\frac{3}{8}$ $\frac{1}{2}$ $\frac{10}{16}$

2. $\frac{1}{6}$ $\frac{1}{3}$ $\frac{3}{4}$ $\frac{6}{12}$

3. $\frac{2}{3}$ $\frac{3}{5}$ $\frac{1}{2}$ $\frac{5}{15}$

4. $\frac{7}{10}$ $\frac{4}{20}$ $\frac{4}{5}$ $\frac{1}{2}$

DEFINITION

numerator The top number of a fraction.
Example: $\frac{3}{5}$

49

Percentages

Learning objective: To find percentages of whole number quantities.

Percentages are simply fractions out of 100. 'Per cent' means 'out of 100' and the percentage sign is %.

We often need to work out percentages of amounts.
For example, what is 20% of 60 metres?
In examples like this, 'of' means multiply, so this is 20% x 60.
Look at these two methods to work this out.

Method 1

If you can multiply fractions, change the percentage to a fraction and work it out:

$$20\% = \frac{20^1}{100^5} = \frac{1}{5} \quad \text{and} \quad 60 = \frac{60}{1}$$

$$\frac{1}{5} \times \frac{60}{1} = \frac{60^{12}}{5^1} = 12m$$

Method 2

The quick method is to use 10% to work it out. 10% is 1/10, which is the same as dividing a number by 10:

10% of 60 is 6.

So, 20% of 60m is double that: 12m

A Write these percentages as fractions in their lowest terms.

For example: $30\% = \dfrac{30}{100} = \dfrac{6}{20} = \dfrac{3}{10}$

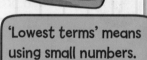

1. 40% ☐/☐ → ☐/☐

2. 10% ☐/☐ → ☐/☐

3. 50% ☐/☐ → ☐/☐

4. 80% ☐/☐ → ☐/☐

5. 25% ☐/☐ → ☐/☐

6. 75% ☐/☐ → ☐/☐

'Lowest terms' means using small numbers.

DEFINITION

percentage This is a fraction out of 100, shown with a % sign.

B These are the marks that Joseph scored in some maths tests. Change them all to percentages to work out which test he scored highest in and which was his lowest score.

Test	Score	Percentage
1	$\frac{7}{10}$	
2	$\frac{18}{20}$	
3	$\frac{4}{5}$	

Test	Score	Percentage
4	$\frac{21}{25}$	
5	$\frac{38}{50}$	

C Write these amounts.

1. 10% of 70cm = _____

2. 30% of 90km = _____

3. 20% of 20 litres = _____

4. 40% of 30kg = _____

5. 50% of 70ml = _____

6. 25% of 80m = _____

7. 10% of 600g = _____

8. 50% of 400mm = _____

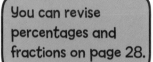

You can revise percentages and fractions on page 28.

D This chart shows different percentages of each length. Complete the chart by writing in the missing lengths.

	50%	25%	10%	40%	5%
60m	30m				3m
50m		12.5m			
300m				120m	
250m			25m		

51

Decimal calculations

Learning objective: To use written methods to add and subtract decimals.

Some decimals you can add and subtract in your head, but other bigger numbers will need a written method.

Adding and subtracting decimals is just like adding and subtracting whole numbers. Just remember that the decimal point in the answer is in line with the decimal points above.

Example 1
What is 12.78 added to 37.41?

An approximate answer is 13 + 37 = 50

$$\begin{array}{r} 12.78 \\ + \ 37.41 \\ \hline 50.19 \\ 1\ 1 \end{array}$$

Example 2
What is 34.82 subtract 19.96?

An approximate answer is 35 − 20 = 15

$$\begin{array}{r} {}^2 3 \ {}^{13}4 \ . \ {}^{17}8 \ {}^1 2 \\ - \ 1 \ \ 9 \ . \ 9 \ 6 \\ \hline 1 \ \ 4 \ . \ 8 \ 6 \end{array}$$

A 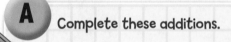 Complete these additions.

1. 45.37
+ 22.46

2. 31.85
+ 52.91

3. 73.02
+ 18.79

4. 64.89
+ 20.62

B Complete these subtractions.

1. 77.86
- 34.84

2. 90.52
- 43.29

3. 65.19
- 27.43

4. 58.03
- 16.25

It is always a good idea to estimate an approximate answer first, so you can check your answer against your estimate.

C

Write the total measurements.

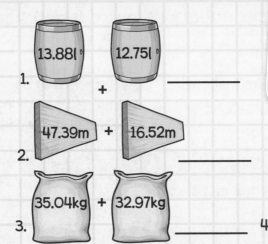

1. 13.88l + 12.75l _____

2. 47.39m + 16.52m _____

3. 35.04kg + 32.97kg _____

4.  59.87m + 21.36m _____

D This chart shows the gymnasts' scores for four events. Using information from the chart answer the questions below.

Name	Horse Vault	Uneven Bars	Balance Beam	Floor Exercise
Eileen	18.10	19.16	18.96	19.36
Sandra	18.40	19.40	19.02	19.00
Nikki	19.16	18.89	18.66	18.96
Julie	19.19	19.26	19.13	19.20
Stacey	19.03	18.99	19.22	18.70

1. What is the difference between the Horse Vault scores of Sandra and Nikki?

2. What is the difference between the highest and lowest scores on the Uneven Bars?

3. Which two gymnasts have a difference of 0.4 in their Floor Exercise scores?

4. How many more points did Julie need on the Balance Beam to match the top score for this event?

5. The scores were each out of 20. How far from full marks was Nikki on the Balance Beam?

Equations

Learning objective: To use simple equations in words and symbols.

Equations have symbols or letters instead of numbers. When you find the value of the letter you have solved the equation.

Remember!

Remember equations need to stay balanced. If you add or take away a number from one side, do the same to the other side and the equation stays the same. It's a good way of working out the letter.

For example:

$n + 2 = 6$ $y - 5 = 3$ $2s = 14$

Use the numbers to help you work out what the symbol or letter stands for. Say it as a sentence and use the inverse to work it out:

"What added to 2 makes 6?" $6 - 2 = 4$, so $n = 4$
"What number subtract 5 makes 3?" $3 + 5 = 8$, so $y = 8$
"What number multiplied by 2 makes 14?" $14 \div 2 = 7$, so $s = 7$

Try working it out step by step.

Example: $3n + 6 = 21$

1. You want **n** on one side of the equation and the numbers on the other. Subtract 6 from both sides. If it was -6, you would add 6 to both sides.

$3n = 21 - 6$ $3n = 15$

2. Say the equation as a sentence: 3 times something makes 15. So $n = 5$

3. Test it with the original equation: $3 \times 5 + 6 = 21$

2s means 2 times s: the x sign for multiplication is not used in equations because it might look like a letter.

A Read and answer these.

1. What number when added to 9 gives 12? _____

2. What number subtract 8 gives 7? _____

3. What number multiplied by 6 gives 30? _____

4. What multiplied by 4 gives 32? _____

5. What subtract 7 gives 12? _____

6. What added to 3 gives 11? _____

7. What multiplied by 4 gives 16? _____

8. What added to 5 gives 14? _____

B Write the value of each letter.

1. $c - 4 = 5$ $c =$ _____

2. $7 + f = 11$ $f =$ _____

3. $16 - s = 9$ $s =$ _____

4. $y + 8 = 14$ $y =$ _____

5. $2t = 16$ $t =$ _____

6. $4m = 20$ $m =$ _____

7. $k - 3 = 17$ $k =$ _____

8. $8 + j = 13$ $j =$ _____

C Work out the value of each letter.

1. $8 + 5e = 28$ $e =$ _____

2. $4h - 12 = 12$ $h =$ _____

3. $26 - 3p = 5$ $p =$ _____

4. $2r + 5 = 23$ $r =$ _____

5. $7v - 11 = 10$ $v =$ _____

6. $9 + 4w = 49$ $w =$ _____

D Write an equation for each of the following problems.

1. Flowers are put in bunches of 10. How many flowers are there in **t** bunches?

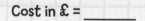

Total number of flowers = _____

2. A ticket costs £**y**. What is the cost of 12 tickets?

Cost in £ = _____

3. There are 25 library books and **n** books are borrowed. How many library books are left?

Books remaining = _____

Coordinates

Learning objective: To use coordinates to draw and find shapes.

Coordinates are used to show an exact position of a point on a grid.
Two numbers from the x and y axis show the position:

Look at the graph.

The numbers on the horizontal x axis are written first, then the vertical y axis. You can remember this because x comes before y in the alphabet!

The coordinates of A are (2, 5)
The coordinates of B are (4, 3)
Coordinates are always written in brackets separated by a comma.

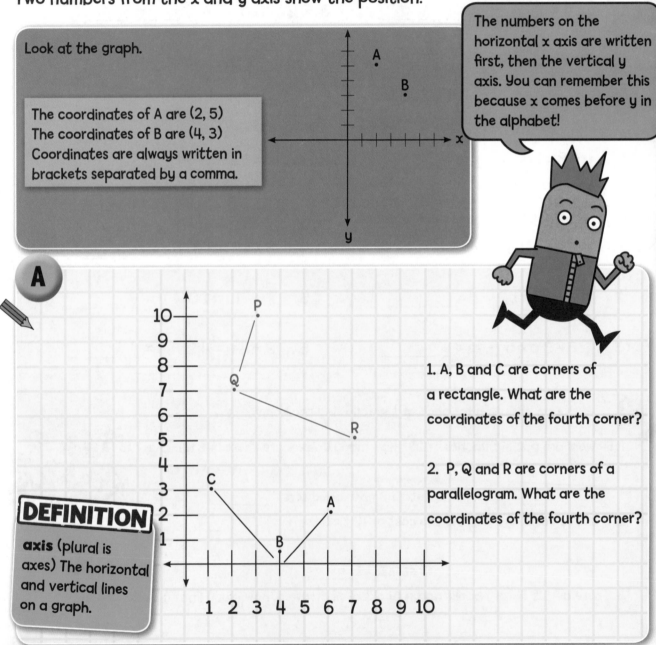

A

1. A, B and C are corners of a rectangle. What are the coordinates of the fourth corner?

2. P, Q and R are corners of a parallelogram. What are the coordinates of the fourth corner?

DEFINITION

axis (plural is axes) The horizontal and vertical lines on a graph.

DEFINITION

vertical A line that is straight up or down, at right angles to a horizontal line.

B

Look at how each of these triangles has moved.

Write the coordinates of the vertices of both triangles for each of them.

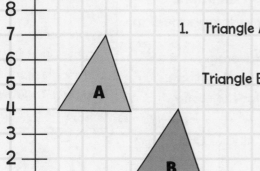

1. Triangle A   (1, 4), (3, 7), (4, 4)

    Triangle B   (_,_), (_,_), (_,_)

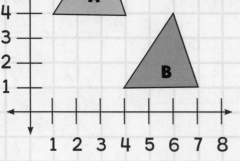

2. Triangle C   (_,_), (_,_), (_,_)

    Triangle D   (_,_), (_,_), (_,_)

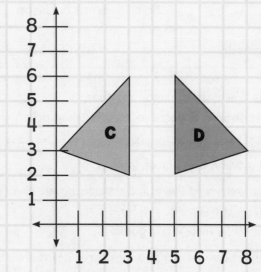

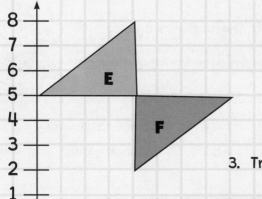

3. Triangle E   (_,_), (_,_), (_,_)

    Triangle F   (_,_), (_,_), (_,_)

DEFINITION

horizontal A horizontal line is a straight level line across, in the same direction as the horizon.

57

Data

Learning objective: To solve problems using the mode, median and mean.

Averages are middle scores or the most common numbers.
There are three main types of average: mean, mode and median.

> When working out the median and there is an even amount of numbers, you take the two middle numbers, add them together and divide by two.

Look at this example to compare the three types of average.
This chart shows the goals scored by the players in a football team.
Does Sam score above the average number of goals for the team?

Player	Sam	Brent	Jason	Ali	Carl
Goals scored	8	4	8	6	9

Mode is the most common number.
2 players scored **8** goals so that is the mode.

Median is the middle number when listed in order – 4, 6, **8**, 8, 9.
8 is the median number of goals.

For the **mean** add the numbers and divide the total by the number of items in the list.
4 + 6 + 8 + 8 + 9 = 35   35 ÷ 5 = 7
So the mean average is 7 goals.

Sam is an above-average goal scorer compared with the mean average,
and at the average for the mode and median.

A

A packet of fruit-drops is divided into piles of different flavours.

| grape (purple) | = 3 | lemon (yellow) | = 4 | strawberry (pink) | = 7 |
| orange (orange) | = 4 | lime (green) | = 8 | raspberry (red) | = 4 |

1. Which is the most common amount of sweets of the same flavour? _____

   Is this the mean, mode or median? _____

2. If the piles of sweets were put in order of size, which size pile would be in the middle?

   _____

   Is this the mean, mode or median? _____

B

These are the heights of a group of five children.

Ben: 140cm   Sam: 130cm   Eve: 140cm   Amy: 150cm   Jon: 190cm

1. What is the mode height?

2. What is the median height?

3. What is the mean height?

4. How many children are above the mean average height?

5. Which child is at the mean average height?

6. Another child joins the group. Her height is 120cm. What is the mean

   average height for the group now?

Remember!
Mode is the most common number.

C

These are the hand-spans for a group of 10 children.

A hand-span is measured from the tip of the little finger to the tip of the thumb.

10cm	8cm	12cm	9cm	8cm	10cm	13cm	11cm	9cm	10cm

Median: _____   Mode: _____   Mean: _____

Challenge

Read this graph and find the median, mode and mean averages of the number of hours of TV watched each day in one week.

Median: _____   Mode: _____   Mean: _____

Probability

Learning objective: To describe and predict outcomes using the language of chance.

The probability of an event happening is how likely it is going to happen. In mathematics we can use a probability scale to show how likely an event is to happen.

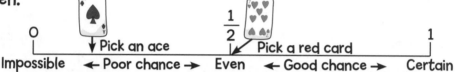

0		$\frac{1}{2}$		1
Impossible	← Poor chance →	Even	← Good chance →	Certain

↓ Pick an ace   ↓ Pick a red card

For example, there is a poor chance that I will pick out an ace from a pack of cards, but there is an even chance of picking out a red card.

Method 1

Even chance, or evens, is an equal chance of something happening as not happening. We also say a 1 in 2 chance, 1/2 chance or a 50:50 chance.

Example: In a pack of playing cards there is an even chance of picking a red card.

Method 2

Dice experiments are useful for testing probabilities.

On a normal die, the probability of throwing a 2 is 1 in 6 1/6. That is because there is only one number 2 on the die out of a possible six

or

0 is impossible - there needs to be absolutely no chance of it happening, and 1 is certain - it will absolutely, definitely happen. Most events lie somewhere in between these two extremes.

A

These ten playing cards are shuffled and placed face down. Write a statement to show the probability of turning over these cards.

Impossible   Poor chance   Evens   Good chance   Certain

1. a multiple of 2
2. a diamond
3. a multiple of 5

4. a number greater than 6
5. the queen of diamonds
6. the 9 of diamonds

B

The ten playing cards are shuffled and placed face down.

What is the probability of turning over each of these?

Write your answers as fractions.

1. an odd number _____

2. the ace of diamonds _____

3. a multiple of 3 _____

4. a number 4 or less _____

5. a number that is not a 2-digit number _____

6. the 6 of diamonds _____

C

Using a dice, write the chance of throwing each of these.

Choose one of the following probabilities →   1 in 2   1 in 3   1 in 6

1. a six

2. an even number

3. a multiple of 3

4. a number greater than 4

5. a number less than 4

6. a one

D

Colour the correct number of beads in this bag to match these probabilities.

- There is a 50:50 chance of picking out a red bead from the bag.
- There is a 1 in 6 chance of picking out a blue bead from the bag.
- There is a 1/4 chance of picking out a green bead from the bag.
- It is impossible to pick out a yellow bead from the bag.
- There is a 1 in 12 chance of picking out a black bead from the bag.

How many of each colour are there?

1. _____ red beads

2. _____ green beads

3. _____ blue beads

4. _____ black beads

5. _____ yellow beads

Proportion

Learning objective: To solve simple problems involving proportions of quantities.

Finding the proportion of an amount is the same as finding the fraction of the whole amount. A proportion can be written as a fraction.

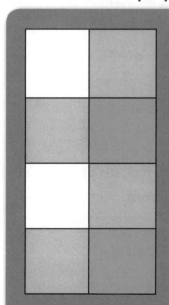

What proportion of the tiles are white?
When you look at the proportion of an amount, it is the same as finding the fraction of the whole amount.
There are 8 tiles altogether, 2 of them are white, so 2/8 of the tiles are white.
This means that the proportion of white tiles is 1 in every 4, or 1/4.

Two quantities are in direct proportion when they increase or decrease in the same ratio.
For example, if 3 apples weigh 300 g, what is the weight of 15 apples?
This is 5 times the number of apples, so it is five times the weight: 300 g x 5 = 1500 g (or 1.5 kg).

A Look at these tile patterns. What proportion of each of the patterns is blue?

1. ____   2. ____   3. ____   4. ____   5. ____   6. ____

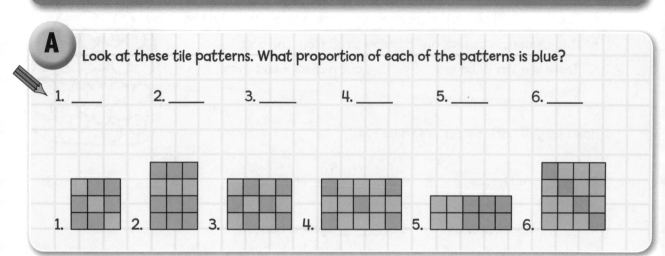

1.   2.   3.   4.   5.   6.

proportion A fraction of a whole amount.

B

Complete these tables showing the proportion of fruit in juice drinks.

Remember to keep the proportion between the fruit the same for each amount.

1.

Pineapples	Oranges	Total
1	4	5
2	8	
	20	
8		
10		

2.

Bananas	Peaches	Total
2	3	5
4	6	
	18	
16		
		50

C

In these recipes the amount of each ingredient is given as a proportion of the total weight.

Write the missing weights of each ingredient in these two recipes.

600g Carrot and Walnut cake

1/4 butter   150g

1/3 flour   200g

1/6 grated carrots _____g

1/10 sugar _____g

1/12 beaten eggs _____g

1/15 walnuts _____g

360g Chocolate Chip Cookies

1/2 flour _____g

1/4 butter _____g

1/6 sugar _____g

1/12 chocolate chips _____g

D

What weight of ingredients are needed for a 1.2kg carrot and walnut cake?

butter _____g

flour _____g

grated carrots _____g

sugar _____g

beaten eggs _____g

walnuts _____g

63

Spelling tips

There are lots of things you can do to help with your spelling.

Learn words in groups. For example:

bright   fright   might   sight

Look, say, cover, write, check:

- look at the word
- say it out loud
- cover it with one hand
- write it without looking
- check it

Did you get it right?

Look for words within words, or words that have a common root. For example:

sign   signal   signature

Break longer words into syllables. For example:

information = in/form/a/tion

Say it as it is spelt, sounding out any silent letters. For example:

knife   comb   February

Use a mnemonic. For example:

'Necessary' has one coffee with two sugars (there are one c and two s's in the word).

Keep a spelling log of difficult words.

Learning the short words first will help you to spell the longer words later.

A

Look at the words below. Can you see any short words within them? Write the short words next to the long words. The first one has been started for you.

caterpillar	cat pill ate	supermarket	super marcket
television	tele vision	subway	sub way
cupboard	cup board	basketball	basket ball
wardrobe	war drobe	crossword	cross word

Some words, called homophones, sound the same but are spelt differently. For example:

bus fare	fire grate	horse's rein
fair ground	great fun	rain water

B

Read the passage below. Cross out any wrong spellings and write the correct spellings above.

On Saturday, we ~~tuck~~ took the train into town. We usually go ~~bye~~ by car because Mum

says the train fair is two deer, but she agrees it's much faster ~~bye~~ by train.

We even had a drink on the train, witch we can't do in the car! We didn't

~~knead~~ need to pay four parking either so I think the train was cheeper in the end!

65

Spelling plurals

Learning objective: To learn to spell plurals.

Nouns (people, places and things) can be either singular or plural.

For example:

one dog (singular)

two dogs (plural)

Remember!

To make most words plural, you just add an 's'.

A

1. To make some nouns plural, you just add an 's'. Add an 's' to the end of these nouns to make them plural.

   banana**s**   girl**s**   boy**s**   day**s**   star**s**

2. To make other nouns plural, you add 'es'. Write 'es' at the end of these nouns to make them plural.

   potato**es**   bus**es**   box**es**   dish**es**
   watch**es**   dress**es**   tomato**es**   brush**es**
   bench**es**   glass**es**   wish**es**   volcano**es**

Learning the rules will help you to spell plurals.

Remember!

When nouns end in 'ch', 'sh', 's', 'ss' or 'x' add 'es' to make them plural. When a noun ends in 'o' we also usually add 'es' — except for 'pianos'!

If you have any difficulty (spelt: Mrs D, Mrs I, Mrs FFI, Mrs C, Mrs U, Mrs LTY) in learning any of these plurals, try a mnemonic!

B

1. When a noun ends in an 'f' sound, drop the 'f' and write 'ves'. Write these nouns as plurals:

leaf › lea _ves_   knife › kni _ves_   calf › cal _ves_

2. When a noun ends in a consonant followed by a 'y', drop the 'y' and write 'ies'. Have a go at these:

baby › _babies_   butterfly › _butterflies_ pony › _ponies_
story › _stories_   party › _parties_   lady › _ladies_

Some plurals don't follow the rules. You will need to learn these separately.

mouse › mice   tooth › teeth   man › men

3. Write the plurals for these tricky nouns. You can use a dictionary to help you.

goose › _geese_   sheep › _sheep_   deer › _deer_
foot › _feet_   child › _children_   woman › _women_

67

Prefixes and suffixes

Learning objective: To learn about prefixes and suffixes.

A prefix is a letter (or group of letters) added to the beginning of a word.
A suffix is a letter (or group of letters) added to the end of a word.

A

1. Read each definition below, and write the missing prefix or the missing word ending. Tele means 'far away'. Auto means 'by itself'.

Another word for your signature.   auto _graph_

A long tube with a lens at the end.   tele _scope_

Something that works by itself.   _auto_ matic

Another word for car.   auto _mobile_

Something that allows you to speak to someone far away.   tele _phone_

Your own life story, written by you.   _auto_ biography

2. Sometimes a prefix is added to change the meaning of a word. If the prefix 'anti' means 'not', what do you think these words mean? Write your definitions on the lines.

anti-ageing   _Not aging_

anti-bacterial   _Not bacterial_

anti-freeze   _Not cold_

B   Which of these things would you expect to find in toothpaste? Circle your answer.

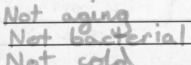

anti-ageing cream

an anti-bacterial

anti-freeze

So, 'anti-' isn't the same as 'aunty' then?!

68

prefix Letters added to the beginning of a word.
suffix Letters added to the end of a word.

C

Complete each of these words by writing the missing suffix at the end. Choose from 'cian' or 'ist'. Then write a definition for each one. The first one has been done for you.

Word	Meaning
magician	Someone who performs magic tricks.
pian_ist_	Someone who plays the piano.
chem_ist_	Someone who use chemicals.
beauti_cian_	Someone who makes make-up.
electri_cian_	Someone who likes eletrices.
musi_cian_	Someone who plays a insterment.
politi_cian_	Someone who is in politics.
biolog_ist_	Someone who studies living things.

A suffix can change a word from singular to plural, but can also change a verb (an action word) into a noun.

verb		**noun**
paint	⟶	painter
dance	⟶	dancer

D

Add the suffix 'er' to change these verbs into nouns.
Write the nouns in the table below.

verb	noun
sing	singer
garden	gardener
teach	teacher
climb	climber
walk	walker
play	player

Punctuation

Learning objective: To learn to use basic punctuation.

We use punctuation in our writing to show the reader how the words should be spoken and to help them understand the text.

Commas are used within sentences to separate items in a list. They are also used to separate ideas.

A Write the missing commas in these sentences.

When Superboy whispered a secret word, his school jumper became a long, shiny red cloak, and his spectacles morphed into a mirrored black mask. His super-human powers enabled him to climb vertical walls, scale rooftops, sense danger and bring wrong-doers to justice.

Exclamation marks (!) are used to signal surprise, excitement or humour.

B Read the passage below and write in exclamation marks or full stops where they are missing.

All of a sudden, the rock door split open and a dark figure sprang out! It was the Evil Weevil, Superboy's deadliest enemy! Weevil eyed him menacingly for a second and lunged forward with a blood-curdling battle cry!

Don't over-use exclamation marks!

Question marks (?) are used
to signal a question.

C

Write a question mark at the end of the sentences
where questions are asked.
If a sentence is not a question, you can use either
a full stop or an exclamation mark.

How was Superboy going to defeat the Evil Weevil? Was he cunning and clever enough to
outwit him? Everyone knew that the Weevil was a wimp really but he was a scary wimp, all
the same What would happen if Superboy failed Would the Earth be plunged into another
inter-planetary war

Remember!

Sentences that ask questions
usually begin with Who, What,
When, Where, How, Why or Can.

Speech marks are drawn around any words that are spoken.

D

Write the speech marks in the dialogue below.

So, Superboy, we meet at last, the Weevil sneered. It's a shame we don't have time
to strike up a friendship! Ha, ha, ha! The Weevil laughed at his own feeble joke.
I wouldn't worry, Weevil, replied Superboy. You'll have plenty of time to make friends
with the cockroaches you'll meet in the state planetary prison!

Remember!

- Speech marks open at the start and close at the
  end of the words spoken.
- All other punctuation goes inside the speech marks.
- Start a new paragraph for each new speaker.

Using apostrophes

Apostrophes are a form of punctuation that can be used in two different ways.

When an apostrophe is used to shorten a word it is known as a contraction. Apostrophes can also be used to show possession.

Examples of contractions:

do not = don't

can not = can't

we are = we're

it is = it's

Examples of possessions:

Sally's shoes

The dog's dinner

My sister's dress

His teacher's desk

Do you know the difference between possessive apostrophes and contractions?

A

In the sentences below, circle the apostrophes that shorten words and underline the apostrophes that show possession.

1. I can't find it. It's gone!
2. That's my friend's house.
3. It's Toni's book.
4. Where's Mrs Dale's class?
5. They'll be late for school.
6. We're going to Gina's party.

B

Write these contractions in full.

can't > _____

it's > _____

that's > _____

they'll > _____

where's > _____

we're > _____

Remember!

The word 'it's' is a contraction that means 'it has' or 'it is'. For example:

It's my bone.
(apostrophe)

The dog buried its bone.
(no apostrophe)

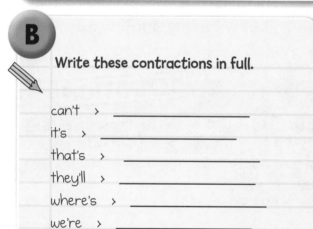

For example, when there is more than one dog you say:
The dogs' dinner

In plural nouns, possessive apostrophes come after the 's'.

C Put possessive apostrophes in these sentences.

1. The clowns car fell apart. (one clown)
2. The clowns car fell apart. (two clowns)
3. The dogs owner went to the Pooch Parlour. (one dog)
4. The dogs owner went to the Pooch Parlour. (two dogs)
5. The girls rabbit ran away. (one girl)
6. The girls rabbit ran away. (two girls)
7. The mans sunglasses were expensive. (one man)
8. The mens sunglasses were expensive. (two men)

Remember!

There are some exceptions to the rules.
For example:
children = children's
men = men's

Other kinds of punctuation

These are some of the other punctuation marks you are likely to come across:

Pauses are marked with ellipses...
"I'd like a burger, fries and... ummm, an ice cream, please," said Emma.

Lists start with a colon:
The meal deal includes: a whopper burger, mega-fries and a drink.

Clauses and conjunctions

Learning objective: To learn about clauses and conjunctions.

A clause is a group of words with a subject (a noun) and a verb. A sentence always has at least one clause.

For example:		
The show ended. (one clause)	'the show' = noun	'ended' = verb
The audience clapped loudly. (one clause)	'the audience' = noun	'clapped' = verb

Two or more clauses can be joined in a sentence.

For example:

The show ended and the audience clapped loudly.

Or:

The audience clapped loudly when the show ended.

Can you spot the nouns and the verbs?

The words 'and' and 'when' are called conjunctions. A conjunction is a word that is used to join together the parts of a sentence.

A

Join these sentences using conjunctions from this list:

> so   and   that

1. It was lucky for me. It was not going to be a problem.

   It was lucky for me _____ it was not going to be a problem.

2. The sun was burning hot. We had to put on lashings of sunscreen.

   The sun was burning hot _____ we had to put on lashings of sunscreen.

3. She clicked her fingers. The little dog began to dance.

   She clicked her fingers _____ the little dog began to dance.

Connectives are words that link together ideas, sentences and paragraphs.

Here are some examples of connectives:

first next finally consequently later suddenly except
meanwhile however when but after although also

B

Read the passage below and underline the connectives.

First, we went to the Tower of London to see the Crown Jewels. Next, we saw Big Ben

and, after lunch, we had a great time at the London Dungeon. Although it rained for

most of the day we didn't really notice, except when we finally got back to the bus

station and had to wait ages for the bus to come... in the rain!

C

Choose from these connectives to complete the passage below:

next first lastly but then

_____ we went on the Ghost Train. It wasn't as scary as we thought it was going to
be. _____ _____ we went on the Rocky Coaster and that was terrifying! We
thought we were going to go flying off the track! _____ we got a real soaking on the
Log Flume and the Crazy Rapids. _____ we had a ride on the Angry Camel and it was
so funny that we couldn't stop laughing.

Pronouns

A noun is a person, place or thing (the cat, the bicycle, Mr Parker, Wales).
A pronoun is a word used to replace a noun so that you don't have to repeat it.

For example, the second of these two sentences uses the pronoun 'he' instead of repeating 'Mr Parker':

Mr Parker is strict but Mr Parker makes us laugh.
Mr Parker is strict but he makes us laugh.

A

Change the underlined nouns to pronouns. Cross out the noun and write the pronoun above it. Choose pronouns from the list:

I	me	you	he	him	she
her	we	us	they	them	it

1. Mr Parker gave Class 5 a detention so <u>Class 5</u> missed their playtime.

2. Our class won the merit prize so <u>our class</u> are going on a trip to the zoo.

3. Chris is team captain because <u>Chris</u> is the best at football.

4. Katie loves swimming so <u>Katie</u> joined the swimming club.

5. I usually like history but today <u>history</u> was boring.

6. We watched a film about spiders because we were doing a topic on <u>spiders</u>.

Possessive pronouns show ownership (or possession).

B

Complete the sentences by choosing possessive pronouns from the list:

mine   his   hers   yours   theirs   ours   its

1. It belongs to me. It's _____.
2. This belongs to you. This is _____.
3. The coats belong to them. The coats are _____.
4. The cat belongs to her. The cat is _____.
5. The dog eats the dinner that belongs to it. The dog eats _____ dinner.

Pronouns never have possessive apostrophes!

hers = correct!   her's = incorrect!

theirs = correct!   their's = incorrect!

And...

she's means she is.

they're means they are.

C

Write three sentences of your own using different pronouns.

1.

2.

3.

DEFINITION

possess This means to own something. Hence we say 'possessive pronoun'.

Powerful verbs and adverbs

Learning objective: To learn how to use powerful verbs and adverbs.

Verbs and adverbs bring action and pace to your writing. Choose them carefully!

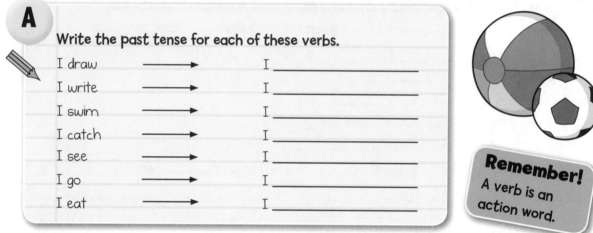

A Write the past tense for each of these verbs.

I draw	⟶	I _____
I write	⟶	I _____
I swim	⟶	I _____
I catch	⟶	I _____
I see	⟶	I _____
I go	⟶	I _____
I eat	⟶	I _____

Remember!
A verb is an action word.

You can improve your writing by using powerful verbs.

For example:
The giant ate the cakes.   (ate = verb)
The giant gobbled up the cakes.   (gobbled = powerful verb)

B Replace the underlined verbs below with powerful verbs to make the sentences more interesting for the reader. Write the new sentences in the spaces on the right.

1. The giant <u>walked</u> across the room.   1. _____

2. "Hubble, bubble, toil and trouble," <u>said</u> the witch.   2. _____

3. The elf <u>went</u> into the shop.   3. _____

4. The vampire <u>got</u> out of the coffin.   4. _____

5. The wizard <u>made</u> a potion.   5. _____

Adverbs usually answer questions, such as How? Where? or When?

For example:

The giant immediately gobbled up the sweets.   immediately = adverb

Here are some examples of adverbs:

really   easily   poorly   deeply   plainly

clearly   happily   angrily   badly   fiercely

Many adverbs end in -ly.

C Add an adverb to these sentences to describe how the subject did something. Use your own adverbs or choose from the list:

quietly   carefully   suddenly   quickly   angrily   menacingly

1. The giant stomped _____ across the room.
2. "Hubble, bubble, toil and trouble," cackled the witch _____.
3. The elf sneaked _____ into the shop.
4. The vampire _____ leaped out of the coffin.
5. The wizard _____ concocted a potion.
6. The boy _____ snatched the wand.

Remember!

An adverb can change the meaning of a sentence.

Adjectives and metaphors

Learning objective: To learn how to use adjectives, metaphors and similes.

An adjective describes a noun.

Clever use of adjectives can make your writing more exciting.

The adjectives in the second sentence tell the reader more about the bird and the nest.

For example:

The bird swooped down from its nest.

| bird = noun | nest = noun | swooped = powerful verb |

The rare, golden-feathered bird swooped down from its rocky nest.

rare, golden-feathered, rocky = adjectives

A Make these sentences more exciting for the reader by adding adjectives. Write the new sentences on the lines below.

1. The car raced round the track.

   _____

2. The pony jumped the fence.

   _____

3. The chef cooked a meal.

   _____

4. The plane landed on the runway.

   _____

5. The artist painted a picture.

   _____

A metaphor is when you replace the subject you are writing about with something else. This helps you to describe your subject using fewer words.

B Write down what you think these metaphors mean.

1. Joe's a sly fox! _____
   _____

2. Jen's a rock. _____
   _____

Metaphors and similes are great fun to use, and they can make your writing more interesting.

Examples of similes:
The giant's hands were like great shovels.

His feet were as big as boats!

C Write your own similes to complete these sentences about a terrible troll. The first one has been done for you.

1. His hair looked like. . . a bird's nest.
2. His teeth were like. . . _____
3. His nose was like a. . . _____
4. His toes were like. . . _____

D Complete these well-known similes.

1. As hard as. . . _____
2. As strong as an. . . _____
3. As weak as a. . . _____
4. As white as a. . . _____
5. As cold as. . . _____
6. As red as a. . . _____

Word play

You can brighten up your writing or add humour by playing with words.

A

A proverb is a well-known saying that expresses a comment on life.

Find out what these proverbs mean and write a definition for each one.

1. Practice makes perfect. When you practice hard you are reworded.

2. A stitch in time saves nine. _____

3. Look before you leap. Before you do something think a about it and get information.

4. Don't look a gift horse in the mouth. _____

5. Too many cooks spoil the broth. _____

Remember!
Many proverbs are also metaphors.

Idioms, or figures of speech, are commonly known sayings that can't be translated literally.

B

Find out what these idioms mean and write a definition for each one.

1. Go break a leg! Do well!

2. To have egg on your face. _____

3. It's raining cats and dogs. Raining hard.

4. We're cooking on gas. Cooking hot.

Onomatopoeia is when a word echoes the sound it is describing.

For example:

pop!

clash!

smash!

bash!

C

Complete each sentence with appropriate onomatopoeia. Choose from:

pop   fizzed   buzzed   squelched   thud   smashed   crashed

1. The balloon burst with a loud ___pop___.
2. The glass ___smashed___ onto the floor.
3. My feet ___squelched___ in thick mud.
4. The heavy door closed with a ___thud___.
5. The bees ___buzzed___ around the flowers.
6. The waves ___crashed___ onto the rocks.
7. The drink ___fizzed___ in the can.

D

Do some research and complete these collective nouns. Choose from the list below:

cows   dolphins   geese   wolves   lions   birds   bees

1. A gaggle of ___birds___
2. A pack of ___wolves___
3. A pride of ___lions___
4. A herd of ___cows___
5. A flock of ___geese___
6. A swarm of ___bees___
7. A school of ___dolphins___

Remember!
Using a collective noun is a more interesting way of writing about a group of animals.

83

First, second and third person

There are three main types of writing – first, second and third person.

When someone writes about themselves using the pronouns I, my, mine and we, this is writing in the first person.

> First person is usually used for:
> • diaries and letters
> • personal accounts of events, activities and visits
> • autobiographies

When someone is writing to address the reader directly, using the pronoun you, this is writing in the second person.

> Second person is usually used for:
> • advertisements
> • instructions and directions
> • discussion texts

When someone isn't writing about themselves or addressing the reader directly and writes using the pronouns he, she, it and they, this is writing in the third person.

> Third person is usually used for:
> • novels and stories
> • information texts
> • news reports

Look for examples of first, second and third person text in comics, magazines and newspapers.

A

Read the three pieces of writing below and decide whether they are written in the 1st person, 2nd person or 3rd person. Underline the pronouns to help you decide. Then write 1st, 2nd or 3rd in the box next to each extract.

1. Palm-fringed beaches and turquoise waters await you on this Caribbean dream holiday. You can enjoy five-star luxury with classic elegance at the Fabulossi Hotel for only $1,000 per person, including flights.

2nd

2. Emily felt betrayed. Lisa was her best friend. They'd been friends since they were four years old and at nursery together. But now she'd seen a note written on a page in Lisa's Pony Diary: Number One: best friend Becky, Number Two: best friend Emily.

3. Just when I thought it couldn't get any better, we scored again. It was a 3-0 hat-trick with only a minute left! Everyone around me went wild, including my dad. It was the best feeling ever!

Remember!

Memorize this phrase to help you work out whether something is in the first, second and third person.

"**I** am first. **You** are second. **They** are third."

Classic fiction

This is an extract from a book called **Treasure Island**. Read it twice, carefully.

... I was far less afraid of the captain himself than anybody else who knew him. There were nights when he took a good deal more rum and water than his head would carry; and then he would sometimes sit and sing his wicked, old, sea-songs, minding nobody. But sometimes he would call for glasses round, and force all the trembling company to listen to his stories or bear a chorus to his singing. Often I have heard the house shaking with "Yo-ho-ho, and a bottle of rum", all the neighbours joining in for dear life, with the fear of death upon them, each singing louder than the other to avoid remark. For in these fits he was the most over-riding companion ever known. He would slap his hand on the table for silence all round. He would fly up in a passion of anger at a question, or sometimes because none was put, and so he judged the company was not following his story. Nor would he allow anyone to leave the inn till he had drunk himself sleepy and reeled off to bed.

Robert Louis Stevenson (1850–94)

This text is written in the first person.

DEFINITION

sea-song A song that sailors would sing, eg a sea shanty.

A

Use the text on page 86 to answer the following questions.

1. Was the person telling the story afraid of the captain?

   No.

2. What kind of person was the captain?

   Curel and a drunk.

3. What did he do when he drank too much?

4. Why did everyone sing so loudly? Explain your answer.

5. What made the captain angry?

DEFINITION

over-riding A person who is extremely loud, bossy and forceful towards others.

6. Why did he slap his hand on the table?

7. Do you think the person telling the story knows the captain well?

Classic poetry

Learning objective: To read and understand a classic poem.

This is an extract from a poem called **Upon a Snail**. Read it twice, carefully.

Upon a Snail

She goes but softly, but she goeth sure,
She stumbles not, as stronger creatures do;
Her journey's shorter, so she may endure
Better than they which do much further go.

She makes no noise, but stilly seizeth on
The flower or herb appointed for her food;
The which she quietly doth feed upon,
While others range, and glare, but find no good.

And though she doth but very softly go,
However slow her pace be, yet 'tis sure;
And certainly they that do travel so,
The prize which they do aim at, they procure.

John Bunyan (1628–88)

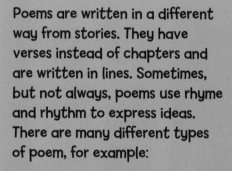

Poems are written in a different way from stories. They have verses instead of chapters and are written in lines. Sometimes, but not always, poems use rhyme and rhythm to express ideas. There are many different types of poem, for example:

- List poem – a poem that lists ideas on a theme.
- Shape poem – a poem that forms a shape on the page.
- Haiku – a Japanese poem with 17 syllables.
- Riddle – a poem with clues like a puzzle.
- Performance poem – a poem that is acted out.

There are many others, too! For activities about writing poetry, see page 104 of this workbook.

Use the poem on page 88 to answer the following questions.

1. Which words in the poem suggest that it was written a long time ago?

2. What is the poet's name?

3. In what year did the poet die?

4. Write two words that rhyme in the poem.

5. What does the snail in the poem eat?

6. What does 'while others range, and glare, but find no good' mean?

7. What does the last verse mean?

Remember!

You can use a dictionary to check words that you don't understand. Taking the suffix 'eth' off words such as 'goeth' will make the meaning clearer!

Poetry: alliteration and rhyme

Learning objective: To be able to recognize alliteration and rhyme
in a poem.

Alliteration is when writers put words together that start with the same sound.

A Write the missing letters in the first verse of the poem below
to complete the alliterations. Then have a go at writing two
more verses. Draw a picture to illustrate each verse.

For example: The **S**nake
Slowly **S**piralled around
the branch.

1. _neaky _nake:
    _oftly _liding,
    _ecretly _pying.

2. _linky _nake:
    _____
    _____

3. _leepy _nake:
    _____
    _____

1.

2.

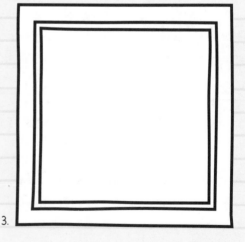

3.

When words end with the same sound we say that they rhyme. Poets use rhyme to make their poems more memorable and to give the words a pattern.

DEFINITION

alliteration
Words that start with the same sound, eg fox, fire, phone.

The Eagle

He clasps the crag with crooked hands;
Close to the sun in lonely lands,
Ringed with the azure world, he stands.

The wrinkled sea beneath him crawls;
He watches from his mountain walls,
And like a thunderbolt he falls.

Alfred, Lord Tennyson (1809–92)

DEFINITION

rhyme
Words that end with the same sound 'rhyme', eg boat and coat, wing and ring.

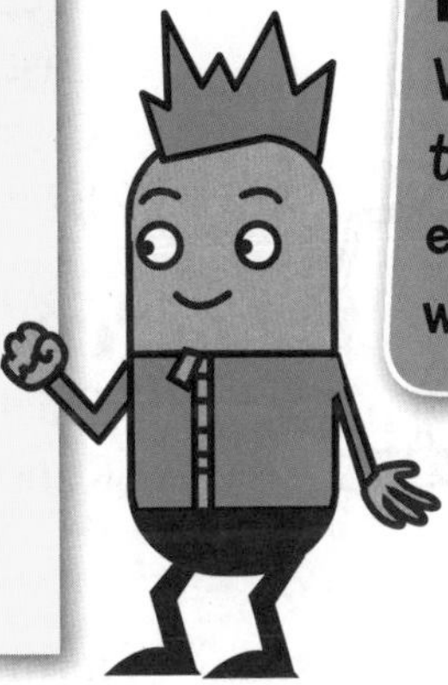

B Read the poem and underline the rhymes. Then read it again and underline the alliterations. Copy the words below to make two lists. Can you add to the lists with words of your own?

Rhymes:

Alliterations:

Playscripts

This is an extract from a play. Read it twice, carefully, and take notice of the way in which it is written - for example, the stage directions are in italics.

Scene 1:
Last Day of Term
Classroom in 31st-century
Britain.

Characters:
Teacher: Number 1471
Robot Assistant: Bot

Narrator: It was the last day of term. Teacher 1471 and his robot assistant, Bot, were getting ready for the day ahead.

1471: *(yawning)* Good morning, Bot.

Bot: *(entering the date on the touch-screen learning wall)* Greetings, Sir, on this the three hundred and sixty-sixth day of term!

1471: Give out the books please, Bot.

Bot: Do you mean those curious, pre-computer-age page-turners, Sir? We haven't used those for over a thousand years!

1471: I know we haven't, but I thought we'd start with an ancient history lesson today!

Rewrite the playscript as an ordinary story text, putting in speech marks
and other punctuation. The first few sentences have been done to start you off.

It was the last day of term. Teacher 1471 and his robot assistant, Bot, were getting
ready for the day ahead.

"Good morning, Bot," said 1471, yawning.

Using speech marks to break up long sections of speech

For example, these sections of speech are rather long:

"Do you mean those curious, pre-computer-age page-turners, Sir? We haven't
used those for over a thousand years!" **exclaimed Bot.**

"I know we haven't, but I thought we'd start with an ancient history lesson
today!" **replied 1471.**

It sounds better to write:

"Do you mean those curious, pre-computer-age page-turners, Sir?" **asked Bot.**
"We haven't used those for over a thousand years!"

"I know we haven't," **replied 1471,** "but I thought we'd start with an ancient
history lesson today!"

Legends

Learning objective: To be able to extract information from a well-known legend text.

A legend is a story based on someone in history or an event that has been retold to seem more exciting. This is an extract from the legend **The Trojan Horse**. Read it twice, carefully.

The Trojan Horse

The Greeks and the Trojans had been at war for ten years. The Greeks were determined to rescue their queen, Helen, who had been abducted by Paris, the Trojan prince. But the Greeks could not break down the walls of Troy.

Odysseus thought up a plan. He ordered a huge wooden horse to be designed so that he and his soldiers could hide inside it. Then the Greek ships sailed away from Troy, leaving behind one man, Sinon, and the wooden horse. The ships lay in wait…

When the Trojans saw the Greeks sail away they thought they had won the war, but they were suspicious when they saw the horse. Sinon persuaded them that it would bring them luck.

So the Trojans dragged the horse into the city. That night they had a huge celebration until finally everyone fell asleep. Sinon released the door in the belly of the horse and Odysseus and his soldiers poured out. The Trojans were killed in their beds and the gates of Troy were opened to the Greeks, who had returned in their ships. Finally, Helen was rescued and Troy was destroyed.

A

Use the text from the legend of the Trojan Horse on page 94 to answer these questions in complete sentences.

1. Why were the Greeks and the Trojans at war?

2. Was Odysseus a Greek or a Trojan?

3. Why did the Trojans believe the war was over?

4. How important was Sinon to the success of the plan?

5. Why did the Trojans celebrate that night?

6. Did Odysseus' trick work?

Odysseus (sometimes known as Ulysses) was king of Ithaca, in Greece. He was believed to be a clever and cunning leader.

Reports and information

Non-fiction is text that is based on fact. Encyclopaedias, dictionaries and information books are examples of non-fiction. This is an extract from a science report about jellyfish. Read it twice, carefully.

Jellyfish

Jellyfish are not fish, despite their name. They are fish-eating animals that float in the sea. They have soft bodies and long, poisonous tentacles that they use to catch their prey and protect them from predators.

There are many types of jellyfish. The smallest are just a few centimetres across. One of the biggest species lives in the Antarctic Sea. Its tentacles can reach up to 45 metres, or about half a football pitch!

One of the deadliest jellies is the Box Jelly. The venomous sting of this jellyfish can kill people. In Australia, the Box Jelly kills up to 65 people a year.

Most jellyfish tend to eat small creatures such as shrimp, plankton and microscopic fish. They wait for their prey to drift by, wrapping their tentacles around them and injecting them with a poison. But jellyfish themselves are vulnerable to predators and are eaten by creatures that don't fear their tentacles, e.g. turtles or other jellyfish.

Jellyfish have no brain, heart or bones, except a jaw! Jellyfish breathe in a different way to humans or fish. They have no lungs or gills. The walls of their body and tentacles are so thin that oxygen is able to pass directly from the water into their internal organs.

When you see jellyfish on the beach you wouldn't imagine there was so much to learn about them!

A

Use the text about jellyfish to answer these questions in complete sentences.

1. Where is one of the biggest jellyfish found?

2. Which is one of the most deadly jellyfish?

3. What do jellyfish eat?

4. To which creatures are jellyfish prey?

Try doing some of your own research on another sea creature, and write a paragraph below explaining anything interesting you have found out.

Rewrite, in your own words, any information you find. Don't just copy the text.

97

Explanation text

Writing that explains **how**, **why**, **when** and **where** is called explanation text.
This is a piece of explanation text about how the Romans built their roads.
Read it twice, carefully.

How were Roman roads built?

The Romans were famous road builders. Some of the roads they built are
still being used today, over 2000 years later. So how did they build their
roads to last this long?

First of all, they would look for the straightest route between two points.
The trees and shrubs were cleared and a ditch one metre deep was dug.
The ditch was filled with three layers.

The first layer, at the bottom of the ditch, was made up of big stones.
This was to prevent the road from sinking.

On top of this, making up the second layer, they put small broken stones,
pebbles, sand and cement.

For the third layer, they cut large, flat paving stones out of hard rock
and set these tightly together in concrete to make the surface of the road.
The road was slightly curved at the top so that rain water would drain off.

Finally, the edge of the road was lined with upright kerbstones.
Major roads had ditches cut on each side.

Diagrams and charts are often drawn alongside explanation text to make the meaning clearer.

DEFINITION

roman A soldier or a citizen who came from the ancient city of Rome, in Italy.

A Use the text on page 98 to draw a diagram that shows how a Roman road was built. Use the text below to label your diagram clearly.

big stones

ditch

broken stones, pebbles, sand and cement

flat paving stones set in concrete

kerbstones

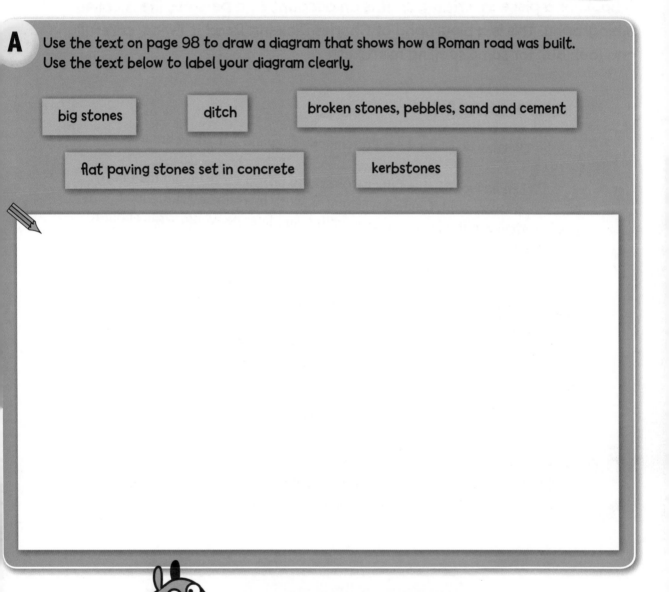

Look for other examples of explanation text in encyclopaedias, reference books and online.

Biography

Learning objective: To read and understand biography text.

A book, or a piece of writing, that is an account of a person's life is called a biography. This is a biography of Charles Dickens. Read it twice, carefully, and look out for some spelling mistakes!

Charles Dickens (1812–90)

Charles Dickens wos born near Portsmouth, England, on 7th February in 1812.

When he wos 12, his father wos sent to prison for debt and the family possessions were sold. Charles was sent to work in a shoe blacking factory. His experience at the factory was appalling and later he would write about it in his books.

Then Charles's farther inherited enough money to pay off his debt and Charles was abel to go back to school. He began his career as a journalist in 1829, reporting on House of Commons debates for a newspaper.

He married in 1836 and his first book, *Pickwick Papers*, was published that same year. More books followed as he became the most popular writter of his age. His books are still read today all over the world. He died in 1890.

A

Use the biography text above to answer the questions on the next page. But, before you do so, look for any misspellings and write the words correctly here.

B

Use the biography text about Charles Dickens to answer these questions in complete sentences.

1. How old was Charles Dickens when he died?

2. Why do you think dates are important in a biography?

3. What was Charles doing on each of dates? (Next to each date write some information taken from the text on page 42.)

   1812: _____

   1824: _____

   1829: _____

   1836: _____

   1890: _____

4. Write a short biography below of someone you admire or know well.
   Try to include some important dates.

Formal letters

This is a formal letter of complaint. Read it twice, carefully.

> 3 Park Road
> Newtown
> Cheshire
> CH32 5RS
>
> Marco Martino
> Manager   8th May 2009
> Excellenti Hotel
> Naples
> Italy
>
> Dear Mr Martino
>
> I am writing to complain about the lack of service and poor quality of the Excellenti Hotel.
>   Firstly, we spent the greater part of our two-week holiday waiting to be served in the restaurant. When our meals finally arrived each day they were cold and inedible.
>   Secondly, we had booked a luxury family room with a sea view but found ourselves in a cupboard that was not big enough to swing a cat in, although we had a wonderful view of the rubbish bins.
>   Thirdly, the swimming pool was more like an over-sized bathtub – hardly big enough for four guests, let alone the forty guests who were booked in at the hotel.
>   Finally, the cicadas made a deafening din, waking us up at dawn each day. No mention was made of these other noisy guests in the brochure.
>   I hope you agree that this is not the kind of service one would expect of the five-star Excellenti Hotel and trust that you will offer us compensation for the disappointment this has caused us.
>
> Yours sincerely
> I. M. Notamused
> Mrs I. M. Notamused.

A   Now have a go at answering these questions about the letter.

1. What do you think the word 'inedible' means?

2. Find an example of sarcasm in the letter and copy it here.

3. Underline the words in the letter used to connect the paragraphs (the connectives).

4. Circle an example of a metaphor.

5. Is there anything about the holiday that the manager could not have changed?

6. Where do you think the hotel was?

A formal letter is always laid out in the same way. Use the template on the right as a guide when you are writing a formal letter.

Write a short letter to the manager expressing the opposite viewpoint about the Excellenti Hotel.

Your address and the date

The person you are writing to and their address

Dear Mr/Mrs/Ms/Miss ...

Use formal language, eg: I am writing ...

Write in the first person, using **I**, **my**, **mine** and **we**.

Yours sincerely ...

Writing poems

Fiction is writing that comes from your imagination. Poems, fairy tales, adventure stories and playscripts are all types of fiction. First, let's look at poems.

> A **haiku** is a traditional Japanese poem that has a total of 17 syllables arranged in three lines: 5, 7, 5.
>
> For example:
>
> | | |
> |---|---|
> | Brilliant blue sky | Brill/i/ant/ blue/ sky |
> | Trees dressed in emerald green | Trees/ dressed/ in/ em/er/ald/ green |
> | Now that summer's here. | Now/ that/ summ/er's/ here. |

A

Have a go at completing this haiku about autumn.

_____ / _____ / _____ / _____ / sky

Trees _____ / _____ / _____ / _____ / _____ / _____

Now that autumn's here.

B

Then try spring and winter following the same '5, 7, 5' haiku format.

_____

_____

_____

_____

_____

_____

A **kenning** is a kind of word puzzle or riddle. It is a way of talking about something without using its name.

Here are two examples:

Blood-sucker   Noisy-barker
People-biter   Tail-wagger
Loud-buzzer.   Bone-eater.

Can you work out what each kenning is about? When you think you know, check your answers at the bottom of the page!

C Try writing some kennings of your own below. Try choosing an animal or a familiar object. Test them out on a friend.

All good writers use their senses to describe what they can see or imagine.

D Use your senses to complete the senses poem below. The first verse has been done for you.

I'd love to taste:

A crunchy potato crisp, lightly sprinkled with sea salt and black pepper.

I'd love to see:

_____

I'd love to hear:

_____

I'd love to touch:

_____

I'd love to smell:

_____

Kenning answers: mosquito and dog

105

Writing stories

Learning objective: To recognize basic plots; to write plans and character descriptions.

All stories have a plot, involving at least one character and a setting.

The **plot** is what happens in the story. Some common story plots are:

1.	Something is lost
2.	Good overcomes evil
3.	Epic voyage or journey
4.	Rags to riches
5.	Comedy of errors

A

Match these story titles to the plots above. Write the matching number in each box.

Cinderella ☐
Snow White ☐
Mr Bean's Holiday ☐
The Lord of the Rings ☐
Around the World in 80 Days ☐

DEFINITION

plot This is what happens in a story.

After you have chosen a plot, the next thing you do is write a **plan** for your story. Think about dividing your story into paragraphs with:

a beginning Who are your characters? Where and when does your story take place?

a middle What is going to happen to the characters?

an end How will the characters change?

The characters in your story have to be believable. They should have feelings and emotions, and also personal motives that cause them to act in a certain way.

Read the character notes for these fairytale characters:

Goldilocks: she was nosy; she snooped around the Bears' cottage.

Jack (in Jack and the Beanstalk): he was poor; he wanted to be rich.

Wolf (in the Three Little Pigs): he was greedy; he wanted to eat the Little Pigs.

B

Write some character notes for these fairytale and film characters:

Cinderella: _____

Puss in Boots: _____

Spiderman: _____

Buzz Lightyear: _____

Nemo: _____

You can bring a book, TV or film character to life by writing a description using powerful adjectives, alliterations, metaphors or similes. For example:

By day, John Jones was an ordinary boy. But at night all that changed. As the red, lycra-suited Spiderboy, he was anything but ordinary. He was a human spider! He could spin a thread as strong as steel and weave a web as sticky as the strongest superglue!

C

Have a go at writing your own character description here.

Writing story settings

Learning objective: To recognize different settings, and write a story setting.

Before you start to write a story you need to decide where and when your story takes place. This is called the **setting**.

The setting creates mood and atmosphere to set the scene at the beginning of the story.

A Think about the different settings you have read about in different stories. Draw lines to match the settings below to the appropriate stories on the right.

fairytale castle or forest

school or home

old house or graveyard at night

remote or faraway place

other planets

Science fiction stories

Adventure stories

Spooky stories

Modern stories

Fairy stories

B Read the passage below. Circle the words that tell you **where** and **when** this story is set.

The summer sun is high in the sky. The crashing waves break against my chest as I race towards them with my board. In front of me, I hear my friends shouting and I taste excitement in the salty air.

DEFINITION

gargoyle A spout in the shape of a hideous animal or human face.
remote A faraway, lonely place.

108

DEFINITION

atmosphere
This is the feeling you create for the reader. It can be scary, funny, mysterious and so on.

Decide on where and when – think about the place and time of year; will it be in the past, present or future? Will it be daytime or night-time?

Describe what you can see, hear, feel, smell or taste.

Draw a picture to help you imagine the scene.

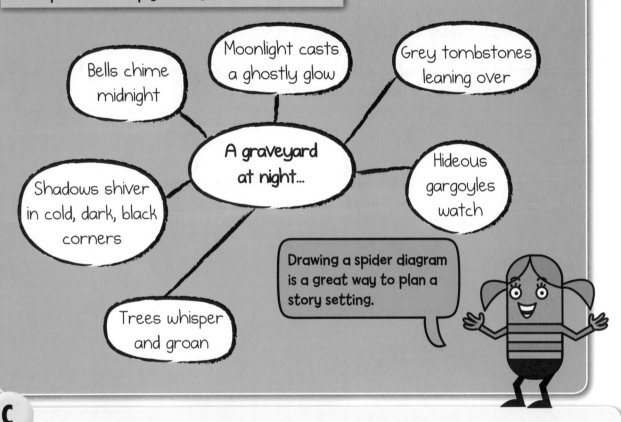

Bells chime midnight

Moonlight casts a ghostly glow

Grey tombstones leaning over

A graveyard at night...

Hideous gargoyles watch

Shadows shiver in cold, dark, black corners

Drawing a spider diagram is a great way to plan a story setting.

Trees whisper and groan

C

Write a story setting below based on a graveyard at night. Use some of the words and ideas from the spider diagram above to help you – and add some ideas of your own.

Writing parables and ballads

Learning objective: To understand about parables and ballads.

A parable is a story about a person who learns a moral lesson. Many religious faiths have parables. For example, the Bible contains many parables told by Jesus.

> Here is a summary of a parable called **The Good Samaritan**.
>
> > A man is attacked and robbed as he walks down the road. Many people pass by, but no one stops to help him. Eventually, a Good Samaritan comes along and helps the man.

A

Try writing a modern-day parable about a Good Samaritan. Use a modern character and setting, and remember to think about plot and character.

A parable is similar to a fable, but a fable has animal characters instead of people. Both types of story have a moral.

A ballad is a song or poem that tells a story.
It has short rhyming verses and often a chorus repeated after each verse.

B Read this ballad. Then fill in the missing rhyming words with words of your own.

Memories of a Norman Soldier

Will I be lucky or will I not
Succeed in helping with William's plot?
Men were facing me with death
My cheeks feel their icy _____.

Chorus:
It was a gory sight
The battle full of death and fright
To see the people suffer so
The victims of the deadly bow!

Now arrows are falling like _____
Surely the Saxons fight in vain
My arrows shoot in to the sky
Towards the enemy they _____.

Harold is now in clear view
In his direction the arrows _____
One has hit him in the _____
For now he shall surely die.

As I watch Harold _____
A tear comes to my weary eye
As I look at what we've done
It's a tragedy, but the war is _____!

By Holly and Natasha (age 11)

Writing instructions

Instructions need to be written in a clear and concise way. Sometimes, when it is difficult to explain something in words, you can use a diagram as well. Add labels and leader lines where necessary to explain your diagram.

How to draw a dog

What you need:
- paper
- pencil

What you do:
1. Draw a faint oval outline for the body and a smaller oval for the head.
2. Draw two small ovals for ears and four thin ovals for legs.
3. Within and on top of the oval outlines, draw more realistic dog-like features.
4. Then add details such as a nose, mouth, eyes, tail and spots.

Start with basic oval shapes.

Add details.

Draw round the ovals to make a dog shape.

This is an example of good, clear instruction text, with a diagram and labels to help explain.

A

Write a set of instructions explaining how to build a sandcastle with a moat. Some text has been filled in to help you get started.

HOW TO BUILD A SANDCASTLE WITH A MOAT

<u>What you need</u>:

- bucket   •   •
- •   •   •

<u>What you do</u>:

1. You will need to use wet sand near the water's edge, but not too close or your sandcastle might get washed away before you finish it!

2.

3.

4.

5.

Writing a discussion text

Learning objective: To know how to write a discussion text.

A discussion is an argument between two different viewpoints.

Discuss: **Is it cruel to keep fish in aquariums?** Read the arguments on both sides.

Yes	No
1. The fish develop symptoms of stress.	1. Vital research can be carried out by observing the fish.
2. Starfish can lose limbs when mishandled.	2. Living in the ocean is more dangerous.
3. Fish don't like to be touched by people.	3. Fish kept in aquariums live longer.

A

Now discuss: **Is it cruel to have classroom pets?**
Write arguments for (No) and against (Yes) keeping pets in the classroom.

No

Yes

Discussion text can be used to bring together all the arguments for and against in a discussion. **Connectives** are used to separate the different arguments. The last paragraph **summarizes** the arguments and states the writer's point of view.

Discuss: **Is it cruel to keep fish in aquariums?** Read the discussion text below.

Many people say it is cruel to keep fish in public aquariums because the fish develop symptoms of stress. **However, experts state** that vital research is carried out by observing the fish. **Others argue** that fish don't like to be touched, and many starfish lose limbs when people mishandle them. **On the other hand, many** say the open ocean is a far more dangerous place and that fish kept in aquariums live longer.

In summary, there are valid arguments on both sides. On balance, I believe aquariums do more good than harm and their research is vital in helping us to learn about fish.

B

Use your arguments for and against keeping classroom pets to write a discussion text in the space below. Read the example above to give you an idea of how to set out your arguments.

Writing to persuade

Learning objective: To understand how to write an advertisement.

Advertising text (or 'copy') is used to try to persuade you to buy something.

Advertising copy from the **Super Sandwich Company**:

Our Super Sandwiches are home-made with special care using only the best local ingredients. You can't buy a healthier sandwich! And there are over 10 tasty fillings to choose from!

A Read the advertising copy above. Look for three things that go to make a Super Sandwich, and complete the following:

Our Super Sandwiches are made with:

1.

2.

3.

Design a package in the space below that will persuade people to buy a Super Sandwich.

Try to include the three **key selling points** above in your design.

DEFINITION

persuade
When you cause or convince someone to do something.

B

Write some advertising copy for one of these products. Choose from:

- A mobile phone
- A toy robot dog
- A computer game

Key selling points:

1.

2.

3.

Now design the packaging for your product in the space below.

Food and the body

Learning objective: To know that food provides the body with energy and nutrients.

The body needs energy. It also needs materials for growth and for keeping the organs working healthily. The body gets all this from food.

Energy-rich foods
There are four groups of energy-rich foods.

Food type		Examples
Sugar	⟶	Biscuits, cakes, sweets, fizzy drinks
Starch	⟶	Bread, pasta, potatoes, rice
Fats	⟶	Butter, cheese, milk, sausages
Oils	⟶	Nuts , fried food, oily fish

Foods for growth and repair
The foods that provide materials for growth (and for repairing cuts and bruises) are meat, fish, eggs, milk, cheese, peas, beans and lentils.

Foods for health
The body also needs nutrients to keep all its organs working well. These are vitamins and minerals. They are found mainly in fruit and vegetables, but also in milk and bread.

DEFINITION

organ A part of the body that performs a particular task in keeping the body alive. For example, the stomach is an organ that helps the body to digest food.

A Make a list of everything you eat in a day. Next to each one write down what the body uses it for — energy, growth or health.

118

Diet and health

Learning objective: To understand that diets can affect health.

A diet must contain a wide range of foods to provide the body with all the energy and materials that it needs. Some diets are unhealthy because they have too much fat and sugar in them.

The body and energy

The body uses most of the energy in food for moving, but it also stores some as fat to keep the body warm. If a diet contains more energy than the body needs, the body stores this extra energy as extra fat. Too much fat can make the body unhealthy.

Making changes

A high-energy diet contains large amounts of sugary and fatty foods. It is easy to change the amount of energy in a diet by changing foods. Sugary snacks like cakes can be swapped for fruit, celery, tomatoes or raw carrot. Fizzy drinks can be replaced with semi-skimmed milk, which also provides vitamins and minerals to help bones and teeth grow well.

A

Look at the list that you made in the last activity.
Does it contain a large amount of energy-rich foods? Make a list of some healthier options.

The heart and the pulse

Learning objective: To learn that the actions of the heart and pulse are related.

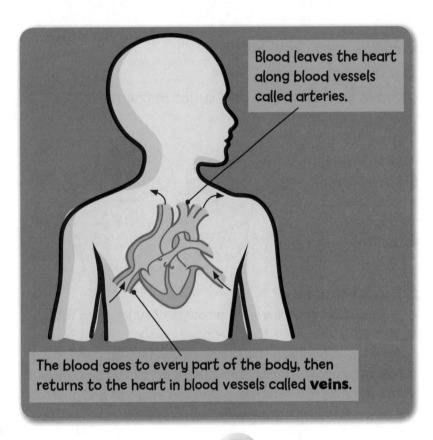

Blood leaves the heart along blood vessels called arteries.

The blood goes to every part of the body, then returns to the heart in blood vessels called **veins**.

The heart pumps the blood around the body. At certain places in the body its beating may be felt as a pulse.

The pulse
You can find the pulse in your wrist. Hold out your right hand and place the first two fingers of your left hand on the inside of your right wrist. Then press to find the pulse.

The heart and blood
The heart is a bag of muscle about the size of a fist. As the muscles squeeze and relax they make the heart beat. This pumps blood around the body.

DEFINITION

blood vessels
Tubes that carry blood around the body.

A

Fill in the gaps in the paragraph from the word list below.

blood   parts   arteries   vessels   veins   pumps

The heart _____ the blood into the _____ and it travels to all _____ of the body. The _____ returns to the heart in blood _____ called _____ .

Exercise and the pulse

Learning objective: To measure the pulse rate and relate it to exercise.

The blood carries food and oxygen round the body. When we exercise, our muscles work harder. They need more food and oxygen, so the heart beats faster.

Measuring the pulse rate

You can measure how fast the heart beats by counting how many times the pulse throbs in a minute. This is called the pulse rate. A watch with a second hand, or a stopwatch in a mobile phone, can be used as a timer.

How the pulse rate changes

The pulse rate is lowest when the body is at rest. This is found by sitting down and taking the pulse for a minute. You can see how your pulse changes with exercise by walking around for two minutes then sitting down and taking it again. If you keep taking the pulse every other minute for a while the pulse should go back to its resting rate.

A Draw lines to match the pulse rate with the activity. The first one has been done for you.

65   person running

70   person lying down

90   person standing up

120   person walking

Pfew! What happens to your pulse when you exercise?

B

Measure your pulse rate when sitting.
Write it here: _____

Measure your pulse rate after walking for two minutes.
Write it here: _____

Predict how your pulse may change after running for two minutes.
Write your prediction here: _____
Measure your pulse rate after running for two minutes.
Write it here: _____

121

Drugs

Learning objective: To understand that drugs can be helpful or harmful.

Certain types of drugs can help the body to recover from illness or injury, but others can make people very unwell.

> If a child needs medication, an adult should always be in charge!

Helpful drugs

When someone is ill they may take a medicine to get better.
Most medicines contain substances called drugs. The drugs may ease pain or help the body to heal or fight infection.

Harmful drugs

Harmful drugs such as ecstasy, cocaine and heroin damage the brain and heart. Someone who regularly takes harmful drugs is an addict. They may need to take more and more until their health is ruined or they die. Some harmful drugs are taken as tablets, but others are smoked or injected into the body. Drug addicts may share needles, which spreads deadly diseases. People who become addicts can get help and recover.

A

Fill in the gaps in the paragraph from the word list below.
(You can use a word more than once!)

drugs   ill   cocaine   killed   medicines

DEFINITION

medication Regular amounts of a medicine (liquid or tablets) taken to treat an illness.
addict A person who feels they cannot survive without taking a certain drug.

People who are _____ take _____ to get better. The _____ can contain _____ to help them recover. Harmful _____ like _____ _____ make people become addicts. Addicts are in danger of being _____ by the _____ they take.

Tobacco and alcohol

Learning objective: To know that tobacco and alcohol are dangerous.

Smoking tobacco and drinking alcohol can be extremely harmful.

Tobacco

Tobacco is smoked in cigarettes, cigars and pipes. It contains a drug called nicotine. People who smoke become addicted. The tobacco smoke damages the lungs, causes bronchitis and makes people cough. It contains substances that damage the heart and can cause cancers to develop in the throat and lungs.

Alcohol

Alcohol is found in drinks such as alcopops, beer, cider and wine. It affects the brain and stops people from thinking clearly and moving about properly. When this happens, people are more likely to have accidents. Alcohol is processed by the liver. If large amounts of alcohol are drunk regularly the liver may become fatally damaged. People who become addicted to alcohol are called alcoholics.

A

Design a poster to discourage people from smoking or drinking too much alcohol.

Parts of a flower

Learning objective: To recognize the different parts of a flower.

A flower has many parts. The parts work together to help the plant reproduce.

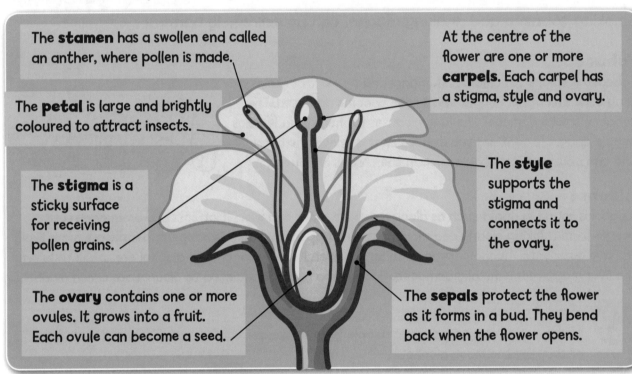

The **stamen** has a swollen end called an anther, where pollen is made.

At the centre of the flower are one or more **carpels**. Each carpel has a stigma, style and ovary.

The **petal** is large and brightly coloured to attract insects.

The **stigma** is a sticky surface for receiving pollen grains.

The **style** supports the stigma and connects it to the ovary.

The **ovary** contains one or more ovules. It grows into a fruit. Each ovule can become a seed.

The **sepals** protect the flower as it forms in a bud. They bend back when the flower opens.

Types of flowers

When you look at different flowers you may find they have different numbers of petals, stamens and carpels. Some plants, such as dandelions, have groups of tiny flowers that bunch together to form flower heads.

A Label this diagram of a flower A to E, using the example above to help you.

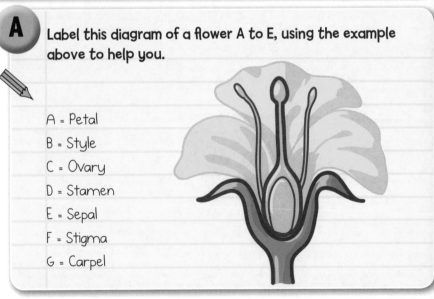

A = Petal

B = Style

C = Ovary

D = Stamen

E = Sepal

F = Stigma

G = Carpel

Pollination

Pollination is the movement of pollen from the stamen of one flower to the stigma of another flower of the same kind. Pollen may be carried by insects or the wind.

Insect pollination

Insect-pollinated plants have flowers with large, bright petals and a strong scent. These flowers make nectar, on which the insects feed, near the ovary base. They make small amounts of large spiky pollen, which sticks to the insect's body as it brushes past the stamens to feed on the nectar. The sticky stigma of the next flower the insect visits collects the pollen.

Wind pollination

The flowers of wind-pollinated plants do not have large petals, scent or nectar. They have stamens that hang out of the flower and release a large amount of small, smooth pollen grains. This is trapped by the feathery stigmas of other wind-pollinated flowers, which hang out like a net to catch pollen as it is blown by. All grasses have wind-pollinated flowers.

> Look at the flowers in your garden or a local park – try to identify the different parts.

A   Tick or cross these boxes – read back through the text on this page for clues.

	Insect-pollinated flower	Wind-pollinated flower
Large petals		
Strong scent		
Nectar		
Little pollen		
Lots of pollen		
Smooth pollen		
Spiky pollen		

Forming fruits

Learning objective: To understand that fruits form after fertilization.

A fruit forms from the ovary of a flower after fertilization.

Fertilization

After a pollen grain sticks to a stigma it grows a pollen tube through the style and ovary to an ovule. Substances in the pollen grain travel down the tube and join with other substances in the ovule.

After fertilization

The ovule grows into a seed. This contains a tiny plant and a store of food to help the plant grow. The ovary changes into a fruit around the seed. Other parts of the flower, such as the petals and stamens, fall away but the sepals may stay in place.

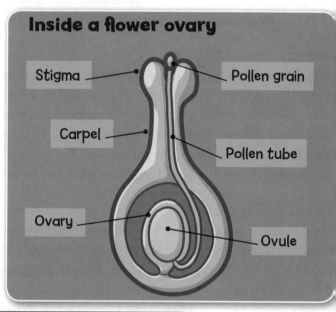

Inside a flower ovary

Stigma

Pollen grain

Carpel

Pollen tube

Ovary

Ovule

Open an apple or tomato. Count the seeds and notice how they are spread out.

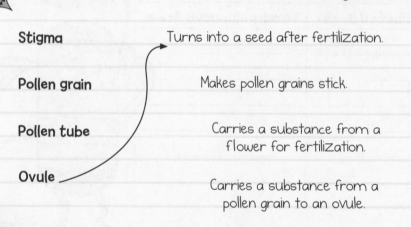

A

Match the plant structures on the left with the description of what they do. The first one has been done for you.

Stigma   Turns into a seed after fertilization.

Pollen grain   Makes pollen grains stick.

Pollen tube   Carries a substance from a flower for fertilization.

Ovule   Carries a substance from a pollen grain to an ovule.

DEFINITION

fertilization
The process in which a male cell joins with a female cell and makes a new living thing.

Fruit and seed dispersal

Learning objective: To know that fruits and seeds can be dispersed in different ways.

The spreading out of seeds from the parent plant is called dispersal. Seeds are dispersed so that they have plenty of space to grow in when they germinate.

Dispersal by the wind

Maple and ash trees have winged fruits. As the fruits fall the wind catches the wings and makes them spin away. The dandelion fruit has a 'parachute', which catches the wind.

Dandelion fruit

Blackberries

Dispersal by animals

Goose grass has fruits covered in hooks, which cling to the fur of passing animals. Succulent berries are eaten by animals, but the seeds pass through their bodies unharmed.

Explosive fruits

When some fruits, such as balsam and lupin, dry they shrink, split open quickly and fling their seeds away.

Lupin pod

A

These phrases summarize the main stages in the life cycle of a plant. Put them in the correct order by writing a number (1 to 6) in each box.

☐ Plant fully grown.
☐ Seedling starts to grow.
☐ Plant makes flowers.
☐ Seed germinates.
☐ Plant disperses fruit.
☐ Flowers make fruits.

DEFINITION

germinate When the tiny plant inside a seed bursts out and starts to grow into a seedling.

life cycle The stages in the life of a living thing.

The human life cycle

From the moment you are born you are growing and changing. In later life you stop growing, but you never stop changing.

The human life cycle is divided into stages.

Baby
A baby cannot do anything for itself. It sleeps most of the time and feeds on milk. After about 6 months a baby learns to sit up, and later to crawl.

Toddler
At about a year old, a baby learns to stand and walk. Toddlers eat a range of foods and begin to learn to talk.

Child
After about two years, a toddler is more skilled at walking and talking — and becomes a child. The child continues to grow and learn many new skills.

Adult
Adults eventually stop growing, but changes continue. As adults get older their hair may turn grey and their skin may become wrinkly.

Adolescent
At about 11 or 12 years girls begin to change into women and boys begin to change into men. The process takes about three years and is known as adolescence.

How do you think you will change in the future?

A Look at photos of yourself as a baby and compare them with how you look now. What are the differences?

Then	Now

Animal life cycles

Learning objective: To compare the life cycles of different animals.

Many animals have life cycles where the young look like smaller versions of the adults. But in some animals the young are completely different from the adults.

Insects

Most baby insects, such as the butterfly, start life as caterpillars or larvae, then change into pupae. Eventually they change again to become adults. This is called metamorphosis.

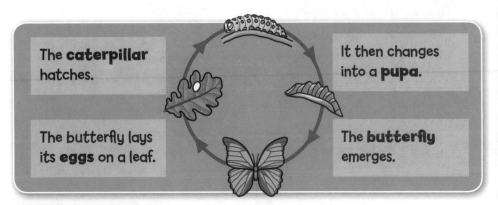

The **caterpillar** hatches.

It then changes into a **pupa**.

The butterfly lays its **eggs** on a leaf.

The **butterfly** emerges.

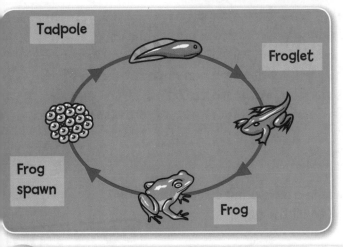

Tadpole

Froglet

Frog spawn

Frog

Amphibians

Frogs and toads start life as tadpoles, but as they grow they develop legs, their tails disappear and their head shape changes.

Life cycles and extinction

A life cycle is completed when the adult animal has young, which carry on living after its parents die. If an animal species is rare and the adults are spread out, they may never find a mate. When this happens, the species may die out, or become extinct.

A

Put these words in the correct places below.

disappears   jelly   hatches   tail   legs   egg

A frog's _____ is surrounded by _____ . A tadpole _____ from the egg.

It has a long _____ and looks like a little fish. In time the tadpole grows _____ and a big head and its tail _____ . When this happens it has turned into a frog.

The air we breathe

Learning objective: To learn that air is a real material.

The air in a room cannot be seen or felt, but when you stand in a wind you can feel it and see its effects as it flows by. Air is a real substance. It is a mixture of gases.

Air has weight

This experiment shows that air has weight.

- Two empty balloons are tied to either end of a stick.
- The stick is rested across two boxes so the two ends balance.
- One balloon is inflated and placed back on the stick.
- The stick no longer balances in the centre because the inflated balloon is heavier.

(a)

(b)

Water fills the gaps

Water pools on the surface when the gaps are full.

Air fills the gaps

Pouring water into soil pushes the air out of the gaps between the soil particles. If you measure how much water you can pour into a dish of soil before the water starts to pool at the surface, you can tell how much air was in the soil.

A These pictures show how much water was in a measuring cylinder before and after it was poured onto soil to fill the gaps.

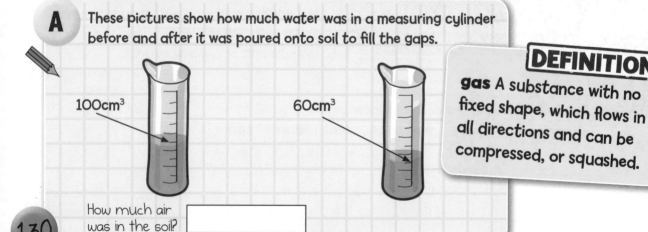

100cm³

60cm³

How much air was in the soil?

DEFINITION

gas A substance with no fixed shape, which flows in all directions and can be compressed, or squashed.

Gases

Learning objective: To understand that there are many different gases.

There are many different gases, and each one has its own properties and uses. The main gases in air are nitrogen, oxygen, carbon dioxide and water vapour.

GAS	PROPERTIES
Oxygen	Oxygen helps us release energy from our food. It lets things burn in it.
Carbon dioxide	We produce carbon dioxide as we release energy from food and breathe it out. Plants use carbon dioxide from the air to make food. Carbon dioxide is squashed into drinks to make them fizzy.
Helium	Helium is the gas used in party balloons. It makes the balloon rise because helium is lighter than air.
Natural gas	This gas is called methane and is made from the decomposing bodies of huge numbers of tiny sea creatures that lived long ago and became covered in rock. Methane is used in gas cookers and fires.

A Match the gases on the left with the description of their property or use. The first one has been done for you.

Oxygen   Used in some cookers.

Helium   Used to make food by plants.

Natural gas   Lighter than air.

Carbon dioxide   Lets things burn in it.

Melting

Learning objective: To understand that solids can change into liquids by melting.

A solid has a fixed shape, but when it reaches melting point it turns into a liquid. The temperature at which a substance melts is measured in degrees Celsius (°C).

Examples of melting

Chocolate can melt in a warm pocket.

Butter melts when it is put on hot food, such as boiled potatoes or toast.

The wax around the wick of a burning candle melts and forms a pool.

An ice cube melts in a glass.

Inside the Earth there are places where it is so hot that the rock melts. (The molten rock bursts through the Earth's surface at the vent of a volcano.)

The melting process
As the temperature of a solid rises close to its melting point, it starts to soften and its shape starts to sag and flatten. At the melting point, the substance flows away.

Reversible change
Melting is a reversible change because, if the liquid substance is cooled down again, it changes back into a solid.

> What do you think would happen to the melted chocolate if you put it in the fridge to cool down?

A Use these words to fill in the spaces in the paragraph below. You can use the words more than once if you need to.

**point   temperature   chocolate   shape
liquid   warmer**

A piece of _____ was left on a sunny windowsill. As it got _____ its firm sides started to sag and it began to lose its _____ . When the _____ reached melting _____ the chocolate turned into a _____ and dripped off the windowsill.

Freezing

Learning objective: To understand that liquids can change into solids by freezing.

A liquid can change into a solid by a process called freezing. The temperature at which this happens is called the freezing point.

Freezing water

Water freezes at a temperature of 0°C and becomes a solid we call ice. The ice has a fixed shape, which it keeps until it starts to melt again.

Moulding metal

Metals have to be heated very strongly to make them melt. When solid metal is turned into a liquid it can be poured into a mould. As the metal cools, it freezes and becomes a solid again. The solid will have the same shape as the mould the liquid was poured into.

Reversible change

Freezing is a reversible change. If a solid substance is heated up again it changes back into a liquid.

A

Substance	Freezing point (°C)	
Beeswax	64°C	☐
Water	0°C	☐
Chocolate	25°C	☐
Lard	43°C	☐
Pewter	240°C	☐

This table shows the freezing points of five substances. In which order do they freeze as the temperature drops from 250°C to 0°C?

Write the order from 1 to 5 in the boxes on the right of the table.

How many would freeze if the temperature fell to just to 30°C? ☐

A substance's freezing point is the same as its melting point.

From liquid to gas

Learning objective: To know that liquids change to gases by evaporation or boiling.

Liquids can change into gases in two ways - by evaporating or boiling.

Evaporation

If water is placed in a saucer, the water at the surface in contact with the air changes into a gas called water vapour. This process of change is called evaporation. The water vapour spreads out in the air. This process continues until all the water has evaporated and formed water vapour.

Conditions for evaporation

Evaporation takes place at normal air temperature but speeds up if the air is warmer or moving fast. Evaporation also speeds up if the air is dry and does not contain much water vapour.

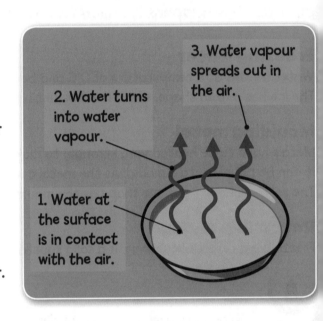

3. Water vapour spreads out in the air.

2. Water turns into water vapour.

1. Water at the surface is in contact with the air.

Boiling

Water boils at 100°C. A gas called steam forms inside the liquid and makes bubbles, which rise to the top and pop into the air.

Evaporation and boiling are reversible changes. Can you explain why this is?

A This table shows the results of an experiment into speed of evaporation in different conditions.

Condition	Time to evaporate (hours)
Cold	10
Hot	2
Still	9
Windy	3
Moist air	12
Dry air	3

What are the best conditions for evaporation to take place quickly?

From gas to liquid

Gases can change back into liquids when they cool down in a process called **condensation**. We also use the word condensation to describe the water that forms on the inside of windows in warm kitchens and bathrooms.

Water vapour and steam

You cannot see steam in bubbles and you cannot see it when it enters very hot air. As the water vapour rises from the spout it cools down and condenses on dust particles floating in the air to make the white clouds we also call steam.

Breathing out

There is water vapour in our breath. On a cold day we can see it condense in the air and look like the steam above a kettle. If you breathe out onto a cold drink can from a fridge you will see water droplets form on the can as the vapour in your breath condenses.

Steam cools and condenses to form a cloud of water droplets.

Steam cannot be seen as it rushes out of a kettle spout.

Condensation is a reversible change. Can you explain why?

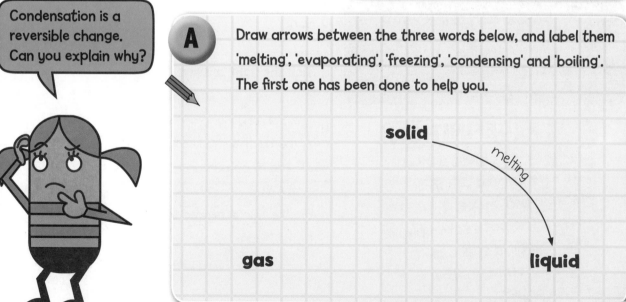

A Draw arrows between the three words below, and label them 'melting', 'evaporating', 'freezing', 'condensing' and 'boiling'. The first one has been done to help you.

solid

melting

gas

liquid

135

The Sun, Earth and Moon

Learning objective: To compare the Sun, the Earth and the Moon.

The Sun, the Earth and the Moon are spheres in space.

The Sun
The Sun is a star. It is made of two gases called hydrogen and helium. Inside the Sun hydrogen is changed into helium. This produces light and heat, which spread out through space.

The Earth and the Moon
The Earth is a planet made of rock and mostly covered in water. The Earth moves anticlockwise around the Sun in an elliptical orbit, once every year. The Moon is also made of rock. It moves anticlockwise around the Earth in an almost circular orbit, once every month. The Sun is many times larger than the Moon, but they appear roughly the same size in the Earth's sky because the Sun is 149,000,000 km from the Earth and the Moon is only 384,500 km away.

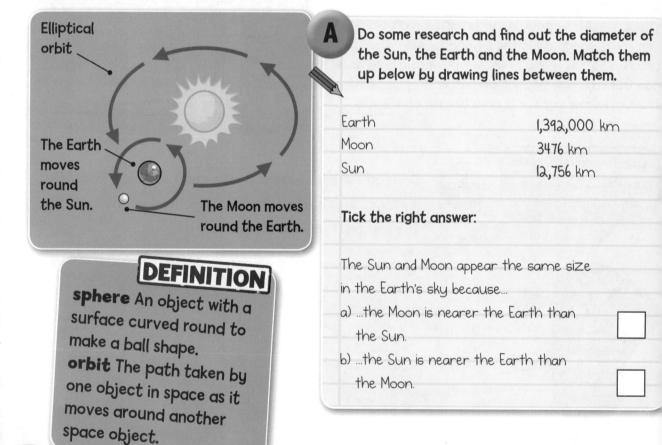

Elliptical orbit

The Earth moves round the Sun.

The Moon moves round the Earth.

A Do some research and find out the diameter of the Sun, the Earth and the Moon. Match them up below by drawing lines between them.

Earth	1,392,000 km
Moon	3476 km
Sun	12,756 km

Tick the right answer:

The Sun and Moon appear the same size in the Earth's sky because...

a) ...the Moon is nearer the Earth than the Sun. ☐

b) ...the Sun is nearer the Earth than the Moon. ☐

DEFINITION
sphere An object with a surface curved round to make a ball shape.
orbit The path taken by one object in space as it moves around another space object.

136

The Earth in its orbit

Learning objective: To link the orbit of the Earth with the seasons.

The way the Earth tilts in space and makes its journey around the Sun produces long periods of certain kinds of weather that are known as seasons.

The Earth's axis

The Earth spins on its axis. The axis is tilted just over 23 degrees from vertical and keeps pointing in the same direction as the Earth orbits the Sun.

The hemispheres and the seasons

The equator is an invisible line that runs around the middle of the Earth. The half of the Earth above the equator is called the Northern Hemisphere. The half below it is called the Southern Hemisphere. When a hemisphere is angled towards the Sun it is summer there, and when it is pointing away it is winter. Spring and Autumn occur when neither hemisphere is pointing towards the Sun.

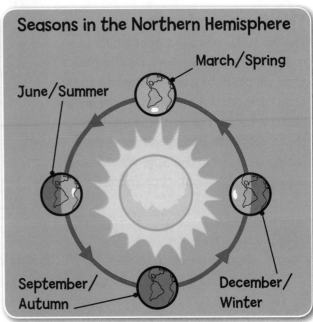

Seasons in the Northern Hemisphere

A

1. What season is it now? Draw the Earth's position round the Sun and label it.

2. Where will the Earth be in six months' time? Make a drawing and add a label.

3. Draw and label where it will be when it is your birthday.

Day and night

Learning objective: To understand how night and day occur.

Day and night occur due to the turning of the Earth on its axis.

The turning Earth

The Earth turns round once on its axis every twenty-four hours. During that time, all parts of the Earth spend some time facing the Sun. When a part of the Earth is facing the Sun, it is daytime there. All parts also spend some time facing away from the Sun. When this is happening it is night-time there.

The Earth from above the North Pole

The Earth turns in an anti-clockwise direction on its axis.

A

Imagine you were above the North Pole in a space ship. Would the Earth below you seem to be turning clockwise or anti-clockwise? Write your answer below.

Look at the places marked A, B and C on this picture of the Earth and the Sun. Read the questions, then write A, B or C in the boxes below.

C
B
A

In which place is it midnight? ☐

In which place is it midday? ☐

In which place is it dawn? ☐

DEFINITION

clockwise The direction taken by the hands of a clock as they move around a clock face.
anti-clockwise The opposite direction to that taken by the hands of a clock as they move around a clock face.

The Sun in the sky

Learning objective: To learn how the Sun changes position in the sky.

The Sun appears to move quickly across the sky. This movement is not due to the Sun. The rotation of the Earth makes the Sun appear to move.

The Sun and shadows
As the Sun moves across the sky the length and direction of the shadows change.

> Try setting up a shadow stick of your own, and watch how the shadow moves.

The path of the Sun

Sunrise in the east

Midday

Sunset in the west

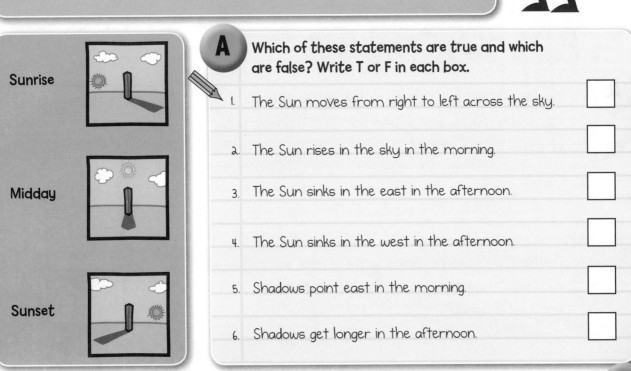

Sunrise

Midday

Sunset

A Which of these statements are true and which are false? Write T or F in each box.

1. The Sun moves from right to left across the sky. ☐

2. The Sun rises in the sky in the morning. ☐

3. The Sun sinks in the east in the afternoon. ☐

4. The Sun sinks in the west in the afternoon. ☐

5. Shadows point east in the morning. ☐

6. Shadows get longer in the afternoon. ☐

The phases of the Moon

Learning objective: To understand how the phases of the Moon change.

The sunlit areas of the Moon we see change as the Moon moves in its orbit.

As the Moon goes round the Earth the Sun shines on half of the Moon. But from the Earth we can sometimes see only part of the sunlit areas. The sunlit areas seen from the Earth are called the phases of the Moon.

The path of the Moon
The half of the Moon and the part of the Earth facing the Sun are lit up by the Sun.

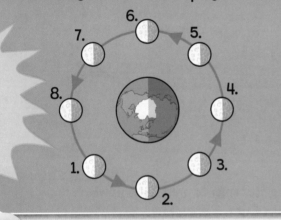

The phases of the Moon
Some of the phases of the Moon as they appear from the Earth.

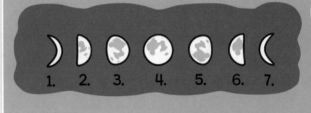

A

1. The Moon is said to be waxing as the phases increase in size each night towards a full moon. Which phases occur when the Moon is waxing?

2. The Moon is said to be waning as the phases decrease in size each night towards a new moon. Which phases occur when the Moon is waning?

Look at the Moon in the sky tonight – what phase do you think it's in?

Solar System

Learning objective: To know how the Sun, the Moon and the Earth fit into the Solar System.

The Solar System formed about 5,000 million years ago. It consists of the Sun, the planets (including the Earth) and their moons, asteroids and comets.

Moons
The Earth and Pluto each have one moon. Mars has two, Neptune has 13, Uranus has 27, Saturn has 34 and Jupiter has 63.

Asteroids
The asteroids form a ring, or belt, between the orbits of Mars and Jupiter.

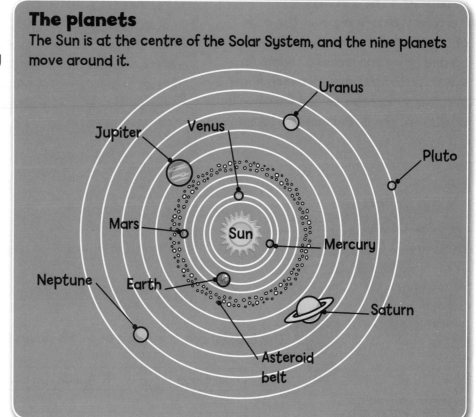

The planets
The Sun is at the centre of the Solar System, and the nine planets move around it.

A

Imagine you were on a space shuttle beyond Pluto and you travelled to the Sun and back. Write down the planets you would pass on your journey and when you would go through the asteroid belt.

* Some scientists now consider Pluto to be a dwarf planet or Plutoid, not a proper planet.

Vibration

Learning objective: To learn that sounds are made by vibrations.

A sound is made when something vibrates. A vibration is a to and fro or an up and down movement. Vibrations can move through different materials.

Making vibrations

If a ruler is held firmly over the edge of a table and 'twanged', it vibrates up and down and makes a sound. An elastic band stretched between finger and thumb vibrates to and fro when it is plucked, and it also makes a sound.

Travelling sound

Vibrating objects set up vibrations in the materials around them. When an object vibrates in air, the air around it starts to vibrate. This in turn makes air further away vibrate and the vibration passes through the air as a wave – a sound wave.

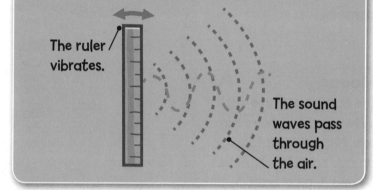

The ruler vibrates.

The sound waves pass through the air.

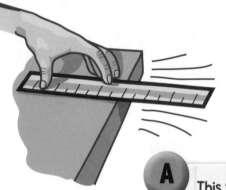

Try twanging a ruler over the edge of a table.

A This table shows the speed of sound waves through some materials.

Material	Speed (m per second)
Air	343
Brick	3650
Carbon dioxide	259
Fresh water	1497
Sea water	1531
Wood	4670

Tick the correct box:

Sound travels fastest through... gases ☐ liquids ☐ solids. ☐

Sound travels slowest through... gases ☐ liquids ☐ solids. ☐

Loud and soft

Learning objective: To understand about loud and soft sounds.

Large vibrations make loud sounds and small vibrations make quiet sounds. When vibrations pass into some materials they may be absorbed so that little or no sound is heard on the other side. These materials are called sound insulators.

Measuring loudness

The decibel (dB) is the unit used to measure the loudness of sounds. Here are some examples of quiet and loud sounds.

Sound	Loudness (dB)
Road drill	110
Vacuum cleaner	80
Busy street	70
People talking	50
Quiet street	40
Whisper	30
Pin drop	10

Guess how loud it is around you now using the decibel scale. Try it at other times, too.

A

Sound insulation

Materials can be tested for their sound insulation properties by wrapping them round a sound source, such as a radio, and measuring the distance at which the source sound can no longer be heard.

1. How do you think a sound insulation test could be made fair?

2. A radio could not be heard 2 metres away when wrapped in material A and could not be heard 50 centimetres away when wrapped in material B. Which material was the better sound insulator?

Pitch

A high-pitched sound is one that sounds like "Ping!" or "Peep!" A low-pitched sound is one that sounds like "Pong!" or "Boom!"

Pitch and loudness

Pitch and loudness do not affect each other. A high-pitched or low-pitched sound can be made either quietly or loudly. Whisper and shout "Ping!" and "Pong!" to check.

Vibration, pitch and frequency

An object that vibrates slowly makes a sound with a low pitch. An object that vibrates quickly makes a sound with a high pitch.

The frequency of a sound is the number of vibrations that pass in a second. Low-pitched sounds have low frequencies and high-pitched sounds have high frequencies. The unit for measuring frequency is the hertz (Hz) .

A

Here are the frequencies of some common sounds:

Sound	Frequency (Hz)	
Baby's first cry	432	
Bottom C note on piano	32	
Cat's purr	25	1
Chainsaw	4000	
Ordinary voice	250	
Thunder	40	
Highest note on piano	4096	

Write the numbers 1 to 7 in the boxes to arrange them in order of pitch, starting with the lowest. The first one has been done for you.

How does the pitch change when you change the length of a vibrating ruler?

Musical instruments

Learning objective: To learn how pitch can be changed in musical instruments.

Each note of a musical instrument is a different pitch from the others. The notes played on an instrument are changed by varying the way in which the instrument vibrates.

Drums

The pitch of a drum can be raised by tightening the skin, and lowered by loosening it. Small drums have a higher pitch than large drums because the skins are made of less material and vibrate faster when hit.

Stringed instruments

The pitch of a vibrating string depends on its thickness (the amount of material it is made from), its tightness and its length. A long, thick, loose string has the lowest pitch. A short, thin, tight string has the highest.

Wind instruments

The pitch made by a wind instrument such as a recorder is due to the length of the vibrating column inside it. A long air column makes a low-pitched sound and a short column makes a high-pitched sound.

Percussion instruments

These are instruments that are struck to produce a sound. They include drums, cymbals and gongs.

Stringed instruments

The strings of some instruments are plucked, strummed or stroked with a bow. These include guitars, banjoes, violins and cellos.

Wind instruments

The clarinet and flute are woodwind instruments; the trumpet and trombone are brass instruments.

A

1. Which drum has the lower pitch? Drum A, which has a diameter of 10 cm, or drum B, which is 20 cm across?

2. Which string has the higher pitch? String A, which is long, thick and tight, or string B, which is short, thin and tight?

3. Closing holes on a recorder makes the air column longer. Does this make the pitch higher or lower?

The growing plant

Learning objective: To learn that a plant needs light, air and water to grow well.

Plants make their own food using energy from the Sun and materials from the air and soil. The food is used for growth and making flowers, fruits and seeds.

Collecting ingredients

The roots soak up water from the soil, and the leaves draw it up the plant. The leaves are covered with tiny holes that let water vapour escape. As the water escapes into the air, more water is sucked up through the roots. Carbon dioxide from the air also passes in through the holes.

Making food

The water and carbon dioxide in the leaf take part in a non-reversible change when light shines on the leaf. The light gives the water and carbon dioxide the energy to make the change – and food is produced. This process of making food by using light is called photosynthesis. Oxygen is also made in this process. It passes out of the leaf through the holes.

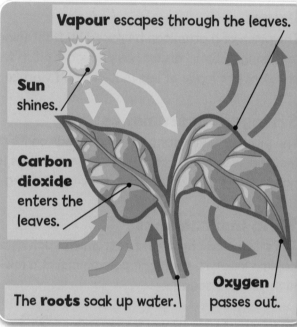

Vapour escapes through the leaves.

Sun shines.

Carbon dioxide enters the leaves.

The **roots** soak up water.

Oxygen passes out.

A Complete the sentence below using the words from this list:

water   **leaf**   **food**   **energy**   **light**

When _____ shines on a _____ it provides _____ for _____ and carbon dioxide to be changed into _____ and oxygen.

What do you think happens to the oxygen made by plants?

Where do you think the carbon dioxide comes from for the plant to use?

Roots and soil

Learning objective: To learn that plants take
water and minerals from the soil.

The roots hold the plant in the soil. They take up minerals
from the soil that are dissolved in the water.

Types of root
There are two main types of root – tap roots and fibrous roots.

Tap roots
A tap root is a long,
thick root, which
stores food and grows
deep into the soil. A
carrot has a tap root.

Fibrous roots
Fibrous roots are long,
thin and branching and
spread out in the soil
around the plant.
Grass has fibrous roots.

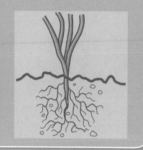

The parts of the soil
The soil is made from rocky particles. The largest particles are pieces of gravel. Sand grains are
smaller, silt is smaller still and clay particles are the smallest. All these particles are bound together
by humus. The rocky particles and the humus contain minerals that dissolve in water.

Minerals and plant growth
All plants need some minerals to grow healthily. Farmers and gardeners add extra minerals to the
soil in the form of fertilizer to help plants grow as healthily as possible.

A

1. How is a tap root different from a fibrous root?

   Soil with lots of large rocky particles drains well, but soil with small rocky particles drains poorly.
   Here are three soils:

   A = gravelly soil   **B = sandy soil**   **C = clay soil**

2. Which soil drains best? ☐
   Which has the worst drainage? ☐

Plant and animal habitats

Learning objective: To learn how plants and animals rely on each other for survival.

Many animals feed on plants, but all animals need plants in some way to help them to survive. Plants depend on animals for survival, too.

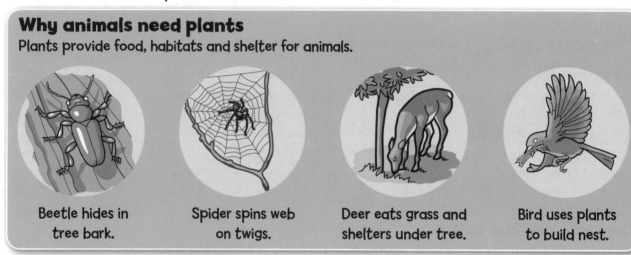

Why animals need plants
Plants provide food, habitats and shelter for animals.

Beetle hides in tree bark.

Spider spins web on twigs.

Deer eats grass and shelters under tree.

Bird uses plants to build nest.

Why plants need animals
Bees help plants to spread pollen. Some animals spread fruits and seeds that stick to their fur or feathers, and many animals eat fruits and spread the seeds in their droppings.

Animal droppings also provide the soil with minerals for plant growth.

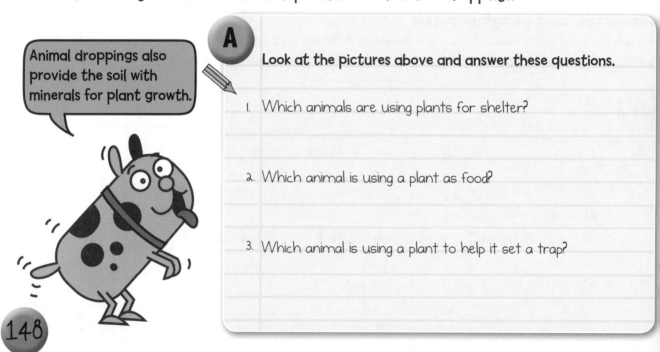

A

Look at the pictures above and answer these questions.

1. Which animals are using plants for shelter?

2. Which animal is using a plant as food?

3. Which animal is using a plant to help it set a trap?

Understanding keys

Learning objective: To learn how to use a key to identify animal species.

A key is a number of features about organisms set out as questions. As each question is answered you move on to the next one until you identify the organism.

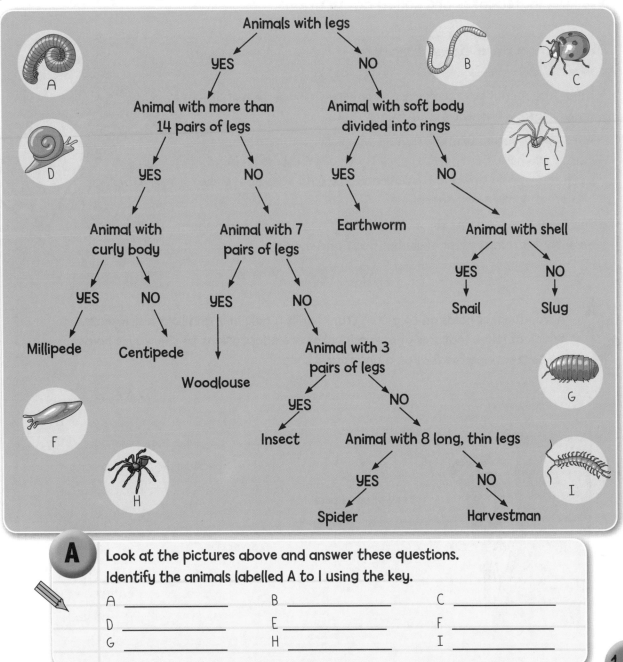

Animals with legs
- YES → Animal with more than 14 pairs of legs
  - YES → Animal with curly body
    - YES → Millipede
    - NO → Centipede
  - NO → Animal with 7 pairs of legs
    - YES → Woodlouse
    - NO → Animal with 3 pairs of legs
      - YES → Insect
      - NO → Animal with 8 long, thin legs
        - YES → Spider
        - NO → Harvestman
- NO → Animal with soft body divided into rings
  - YES → Earthworm
  - NO → Animal with shell
    - YES → Snail
    - NO → Slug

A Look at the pictures above and answer these questions.
Identify the animals labelled A to I using the key.

A _____   B _____   C _____

D _____   E _____   F _____

G _____   H _____   I _____

Adaptation

Learning objective: To know that living things adapt to survive in their habitats.

Living things have body features that help them to survive in a certain habitat. These special features are called adaptations.

Adapting to a pond habitat

- A fish has overlapping scales and is covered in slime to help it move easily through the water as it swims.
- A frog has webbed feet to push on the water and powerful leg muscles to help it swim quickly. Its eyes are on top of its head so that it can lie safely underwater and pop its eyes above the surface to look for predators.
- The heron has long legs for wading in deep water and a long, sharp beak that is adapted for stabbing frogs and fish.

A A woodpecker holds on to a tree trunk, drills a hole in it and licks out insects. Which of these features of a woodpecker are adaptations to the way it holds on to trees and feeds? Put a ring round them.

Two wings

two eyes

lays eggs

stiff tail feathers

two toes pointing backwards instead of one

chisel-shaped beak

makes a harsh call

strong skull

strong claws

long tongue

feathery crest on head

Food chains

Learning objective: To learn that living things in a habitat are linked by food chains.

Food passes through a habitat along links called food chains.

Link 1
Any part of a plant, such as a seed or leaves, may start a food chain.

Link 2
A plant-eating animal, such as a snail, beetle, rabbit or deer. It is a herbivore, or primary consumer.

Link 3
An animal that eats other animals, such as a spider, frog or shrew. It is a carnivore, or secondary consumer.

Link 4
A large carnivore, such as a fox, owl or heron, which eats smaller carnivores. It is a tertiary consumer.

Prey and predator

An animal that is eaten by another animal is called the prey. The animal that eats the prey is called a predator. A predator is always a carnivore, but prey can be either herbivores or carnivores.

A simple food chain

Lettuce leaf   Slug   Frog   Heron

Remember!
In a food chain, the arrow goes from the food to the feeder.

A

Make a food chain using these organisms:

beetle   **seed**   **owl**   **shrew**

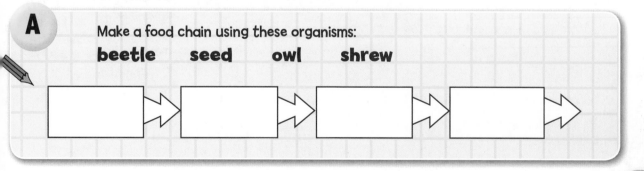

Micro-organisms

Micro-organisms are also called microbes. There are three different kinds of micro-organism - viruses, bacteria and some types of fungi.

Viruses

Viruses cause diseases such as colds, influenza, chicken pox, measles and rabies.

Achoo! A cold cannot be cured with antibiotics because it is a virus.

Bacteria

Many bacteria feed on the remains of dead plants and animals and on animal waste. They are essential in recycling the materials from which living things are made. Some bacteria cause diseases like cholera, typhoid and food poisoning — and some can cause tooth decay.

Fungi

Moulds and yeast are fungi. Moulds spread in air as tiny particles called spores. When a spore lands on a suitable surface it grows threads and makes a fuzzy patch that we can see. Moulds are important in recycling materials for living things, but they can make good food turn bad.

A

1. What kind of microbe might give you a cold?

2. What kind of microbe is removed when you clean your teeth?

3. What kind of microbe might be seen growing on an orange?

4. What kind of microbe makes the contents of a compost bin rot?

DEFINITION

fungi A plant-like organism that does not make its own food but feeds on other materials made by plants and animals.

Living with microbes

Learning objective: To understand that microbes can be either harmful or useful.

Microbes are everywhere – in air, water and on all kinds of surfaces. We can fight or control the harmful ones and use some others to make food.

Preventing and fighting disease

Stop microbes spreading	If you have a cold, cough or sneeze into a handkerchief. Always wash hands before eating. Keep rubbish covered to stop flies getting to it.
Keep clean	Make sure kitchen, cutlery and crockery are clean. Clean your teeth at least twice a day.
Vaccination	Vaccinate against serious diseases.
Medicines	Some infections caused by harmful bacteria can be cured by taking medicines called antibiotics.

Microbes in food

Certain kinds of harmless bacteria are added to warm milk to make cheese and yoghurt. Harmless moulds may also be added to some cheeses to make them 'blue' and add extra flavour.

Yeast is a microbe that is mixed with flour, sugar and water to make dough. The yeast microbes feed on sugar and produce bubbles in the dough, which gives bread its spongy texture and make it rise.

A What do you think would happen if a bread-making mixture contained only water, flour and yeast?

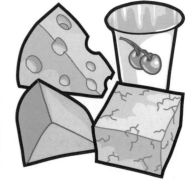

153

Dissolving and filtering

Learning objective: To learn that some solutions cannot be separated by filtering.

When some substances are mixed with water, they dissolve in it. Other substances do not dissolve, and they can be separated from the water by filtering.

Dissolving

When a solid dissolves it breaks up into tiny particles that can only be seen with a very powerful microscope. The mixture of water and the dissolved substance is called a solution. If the solid is coloured, like coffee granules, its colour spreads out through the water.

Filtering

A filter can be used to separate a mixture that contains a liquid and solid particles that have not dissolved in it. The liquid passes through the holes in the filter and the solid particles remain behind. A filter cannot be used to separate a dissolved solid from a solution.

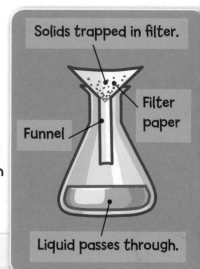

Solids trapped in filter.

Filter paper

Funnel

Liquid passes through.

A This table shows the results of an experiment in which different substances were added to water.

Substance	Dissolved
Sand	No
Sugar	Yes
Bath salts	Yes
Flour	No
Custard powder	No
Table salt	Yes

1. Which substances can be separated from the water by filtering?

2. Look at the picture above. Can you describe how a filter works?

Recovering dissolved solids

Learning objective: To learn what happens when water in a solution is changed to gas.

Water is changed into a gas by evaporation and by boiling. If the water contains dissolved solids, they remain behind because they do not change into a gas.

Separation

If a solution is left to evaporate, the dissolved solids will remain behind in the bottom of the container. If a solution is boiled for long enough, all of the water will change to steam, and the solid that was dissolved is left behind.

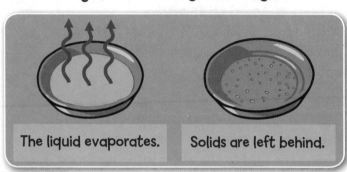

The liquid evaporates.   Solids are left behind.

Steam condenses on cool surface.

Steam rises from the boiling water.

Condensation

If a cold surface is held over boiling water, the steam hits it and cools quickly. It condenses and forms a liquid - water. If the steam came from a solution, the condensed water will be pure because none of the dissolved solid will be present.

A   Use these words to fill in the spaces in the paragraph below. You can use each word more than once if you need to.

salt   dissolves   boiled   steam   cooling   condensing

When _____ is mixed with water it _____ and makes a solution. If the solution is _____ the water turns to _____ and leaves the _____ behind. The _____ can be turned to water again by _____ it down in a process called _____.

The speed of dissolving

Learning objective: To understand that the speed of dissolving can vary.

The speed of dissolving is affected by the amount of stirring, the temperature of the water and the size of the particles entering the water.

When a solid dissolves

When a solid dissolves it breaks up into tiny particles. These fill up the gaps between the water particles.

Stirring, size and temperature

The effect of stirring can be investigated by adding the solid to the water without stirring and timing how long it takes to dissolve. The experiment can then be repeated with the mixture being stirred slowly, then repeated again stirring more quickly. The results can then be compared.

    The effect of particle size can be tested by using caster sugar (small particles), granulated sugar (medium-sized particles), then a sugar lump (large particle) - then comparing the results.

    The effect of water temperature can be tested by repeating the experiment using cold, warm, then hot water. The temperature should be taken before the solid is added.

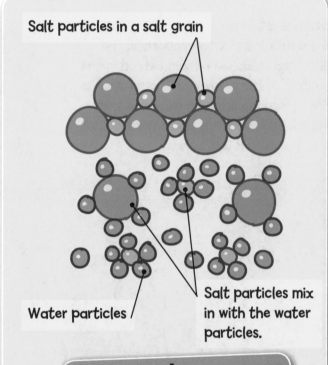

Salt particles in a salt grain

Water particles

Salt particles mix in with the water particles.

Remember!

For a test on the speed of dissolving to be fair, the same amount of solid and liquid must be used throughout.

A

For the tests described above to be completely fair, which of these statements are correct? Tick or cross in the boxes.

1. In the stirring test the size of particles should be the same size.
2. In the stirring test the temperature of the water should be the same.
3. In the particle size test the same volume of sugar should be used each time.
4. In the temperature test the water should be stirred at the same speed each time.

Charts and graphs

DEFINITION

data Information, often in the form of measurements, that is obtained from experiments.

Some data is best displayed as a bar chart, while other data is best displayed by a line graph.

Using a bar chart

A bar chart is best when the data has a few definite values, such as sugar particle size.

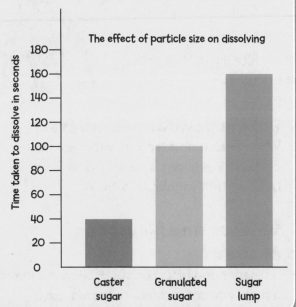

The effect of particle size on dissolving

Using a line graph

A line graph is best when the data have a wide range of values, such as temperature.

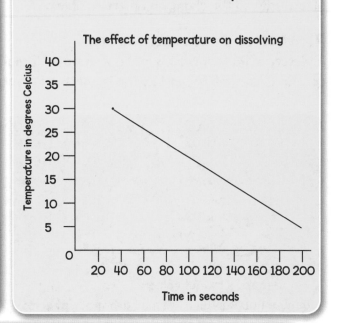

The effect of temperature on dissolving

A   Look at the graphs above and answer these questions.

1.   How long did it take for the caster sugar to dissolve?

2.   How long does it take for the solid to dissolve at 30 degrees Celsius?

3.   What is the water temperature when a solid takes 100 seconds to dissolve?

157

Irreversible changes

Learning objective: To know that some changes to materials cannot be reversed.

Some changes are irreversible. This means that the materials that took part in a process cannot be recovered easily.

Flour and water

When flour is added to water it makes a sticky dough. The water cannot easily be separated from the flour again afterwards, so the change is an irreversible one.

Ouch! Plaster of Paris is used to make casts for broken arms and legs.

Plaster of Paris and water

If plaster of Paris powder is mixed with water it makes a white liquid that sets to a hard, solid white plaster. This is another irreversible change.

If you make a model volcano with a hole in the centre you can fill it with bicarbonate of soda and vinegar – and create a mini eruption!

Baking powder and water

When baking powder and water are mixed, carbon dioxide gas is made, which forms bubbles that escape into the air.

Vinegar and bicarbonate of soda

If vinegar and bicarbonate of soda are mixed a huge amount of carbon dioxide gas is produced, which makes the mixture froth and fizz before it escapes into the air.

A Which substance:

1. ... makes bubbles of carbon dioxide gas with water?

2. ... makes a sticky dough with water?

3. ... makes a white solid with water?

Heating and burning

Learning objective: To know that heating and burning can cause irreversible changes.

When a substance is heated its temperature rises.
If the temperature rises high enough the substance may burst into flame.
When this happens the substance is said to be burning.

Heating

When food is cooked irreversible changes take place.Clay is soft and can be shaped. But when it is heated strongly in a kiln it becomes hard and rigid and cannot be softened again.

Burning

Wood (a solid) burns away to make ash (solid), smoke (tiny solid particles), water vapour (gas) and carbon dioxide (gas). As candle wax burns it changes into carbon dioxide (gas) and water vapour (gas).

A

1. What two things do both wood and a candle make as they burn?

2. Which are reversible and which are irreversible changes? Tick the correct columns.

Process	Reversible	Irreversible
Melting of wax		
Burning of wood		
Baking bread		
Freezing water		
Mixing flour and water		

Look at some meat and vegetables before and after they are cooked. How do they change?

Gravity

The force of gravity acts between everything in the Universe, and creates a force called weight.

Gravity and the Universe

The force of gravity acts between every two objects in the Universe. Its effects can only be seen and felt if one of the objects is small (like you) and the other is very large (like the Earth). Gravity acts between the Sun and the planets and keeps them in their orbits.

When you jump up into the air the force of gravity pulls you back down to the ground again.

Gravity on Earth

The force of gravity acts between everything on the Earth's surface and the centre of the Earth. The pull of gravity on your body also makes your body push downwards on things below it. We call this pushing force weight.

Gravity on the Moon

The Moon is smaller than the Earth, and its pull on astronauts who visit it is smaller than the pull of the Earth's gravity. This makes the astronauts weigh six times less than they do on Earth.

A Can you answer these questions about gravity? Write your answers in the spaces below.

1. Can you explain why things fall down holes?

2. If an astronaut weighs 660 Newtons on Earth, how much would he weigh on the Moon?

3. A rock on the Moon weighs 10 newtons. How much would it weigh on Earth?

Two forces in action

Learning objective: To know that more than one force can act on an object at once.

If you hold this book, gravity pulls it down and the forces in your muscles push it up.

Force meter

The weight of an object suspended from a force meter makes the spring inside it stretch until its tension force pulls up with the same strength. The weight of the object can then be read on the scale on the side of the force meter.

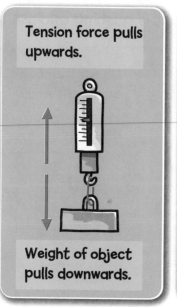

Tension force pulls upwards.

Weight of object pulls downwards.

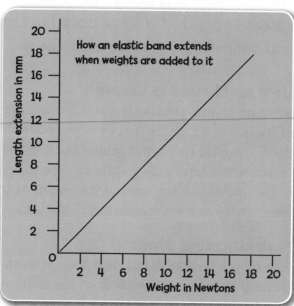

How an elastic band extends when weights are added to it

Length extension in mm

Weight in Newtons

Magnetic force

When a paper clip is put on the end of the magnet it does not fall away, because the pull of the magnetic force matches the pull of gravity.

A

An elastic band was held up and weights were added to it. After each weight was added the length of the elastic band was measured. The results were plotted on the line graph above.

1. What does the graph show?

2. How much is the elastic band stretched when the weight is 6 Newtons?

3. What weight is added to make the elastic band stretch to 12 mm?

4. There isn't a reading for when a 20 Newton weight was attached. Can you guess why?

Upthrust

Learning objective: To learn that water pushes upwards on objects placed in it.

When an object is placed in water it appears to lose weight. What is really happening is that a force called upthrust is pushing against the object's weight and cancelling out some of its force.

How upthrust is caused

When an object is placed in water it pushes some of the water out of the way to make space for itself. This displaced water pushes back on the object with a force called upthrust. The strength of the upthrust is the same as the weight of the water that has been pushed out of the way.

Floating and sinking

If an object's weight is less than the upthrust, it floats. If its weight is greater than the upthrust, the object sinks.

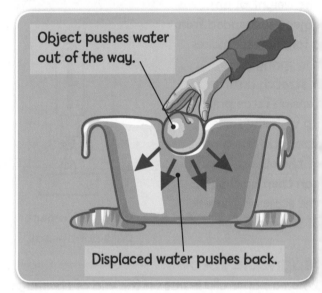

Object pushes water out of the way.

Displaced water pushes back.

A

Six objects were put in water. This table shows their weight and upthrust in Newtons (N).

Object	Weight (N)	Upthrust (N)
1	50	60
2	45	30
3	6	10
4	25	29
5	73	69
6	105	128

1. Which objects floated?
2. What would happen to object 4 if its weight was increased to 35N?

Air resistance

Learning objective: To know that air resistance pushes on objects that move through it.

The strength of the air resistance on an object depends on the size of its surface area pushing through the air.

Gravity and air resistance

When an object falls gravity pulls it down and air resistance pushes upwards on it.

Testing falling spinners

You can make a spinner by cutting and folding a piece of paper and attaching a paper clip to the lower end to help it fall and spin.

1. Mark these lines on a piece of A4 paper.

2. Cut along the solid lines and fold along the dashed lines.

3. Attach the paperclip weight and test your spinner.

The effect of wing size can be investigated by making spinners with differently sized wings then letting them fall from the same height and timing how long they take to reach the ground.

A

Three spinners were dropped five times and their falls were timed.

Spinner wing length (cm)	Trial 1 fall (secs)	Trial 2 fall (secs)	Trial 3 fall (secs)	Trial 4 fall (secs)	Trial 5 fall (secs)	Average fall (secs)
3	2	3	4	2	4	
6	4	5	6	5	5	
10	7	8	6	8	6	

1. Fill in the average time for each spinner to fall (add up the fall times of each one and divide by 5).

2. What do the results show?

3. How can the result be explained?

Light rays

Learning objective: To understand that light rays travel from a light source.

Light sources send out light rays which allow us to see. When light rays enter our eyes we see.

Light ray

Light rays travel in straight lines. A light ray can be made by cutting a slit in a piece of card, sticking the card on the front of a torch, then shining the torch across a piece of paper. A light ray is drawn in a diagram as an arrow showing the direction it is travelling.

Light ray and a mirror

If a mirror is placed on the paper and the torch is shone at it from one side, a light ray is seen coming from the mirror. This is a reflected light ray.

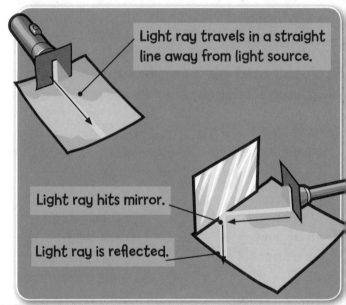

Light ray travels in a straight line away from light source.

Light ray hits mirror.

Light ray is reflected.

A

In the space below draw a light ray coming from a torch onto a book and being reflected into an eye. Make sure you add the arrows correctly. Also add labels to explain what's happening.

Reflected light

Learning objective: To know that different surfaces reflect light
in different ways.

The angle at which a light ray strikes a mirror affects the angle at which the
reflected light ray leaves it. The power of a surface to reflect light depends on
the material from which it is made.

Comparing angles

Lines can be drawn on paper to show the
path of the striking (or incident) ray, the
reflected ray and the surface of the mirror.
A line called the normal is drawn at right
angles to the mirror where the two rays
meet. A protractor can be used to measure
the angles of the rays from the normal.

Comparing surfaces

The reflective power of different surfaces
can be compared by shining a torch on
to them and comparing the brightness
of the light reflected.

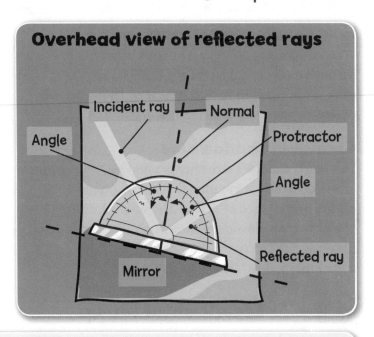

Overhead view of reflected rays

Incident ray — Normal — Protractor — Angle — Angle — Reflected ray — Mirror

A

This table shows the results of two complete measurements and two missing measurements.

1. Can you predict and fill in the missing measurements below?

Angle of incident ray	Angle of reflected ray
20	20
30	
63	63
	77

2. How do the two angles compare? Can you explain why?

Shadows

Learning objective: To learn how shadows form and how their size can change.

A shadow forms when light rays are stopped from travelling. Its size depends on the position of the light source and screen.

How shadows are made

When a light ray strikes an opaque object, its path is blocked. This means there is an absence of light on the other side of the object. We see this as a shadow.

Changing shadow size

The way a shadow's size changes can be investigated by lining up a torch, an opaque object and a piece of paper (the screen). The object is then moved backwards and forwards between the torch and the screen – and the size of its shadow is compared.

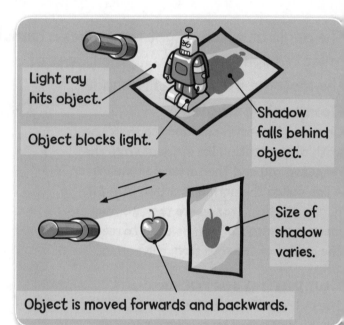

Light ray hits object.

Object blocks light.

Shadow falls behind object.

Size of shadow varies.

Object is moved forwards and backwards.

A

Experimental set-up	Width of shadow (cm)
Object halfway between torch and screen	10
Torch moved closer to object	15
Torch moved away from object	7
Screen moved closer to object	9
Screen moved away from object	16
Object moved nearer screen	6

1. Predict the size of the shadow when the object is moved away from the screen. Does it become larger or smaller?

2. How can the size of the object's shadow be increased?

DEFINITION

opaque
A material or object that does not allow light to pass through.

screen A surface onto which light is shone.

Shadows and reflections

Learning objective: To be able to compare shadows and reflections.

Shadows and reflections have different appearances.

Shadows

A shadow has an outline. This is made by rays of light, which pass over the edges of the object and shine onto the surface behind. Inside the outline it is dark. No features on the object's surface can be seen in the shadow.

Reflections

When light rays strike a very smooth surface they all change direction together. When the light reaches your eyes you can see a picture in the shiny surface. This picture is called a reflection. Scientists call it an image. The image is a picture of where the light rays came from before they hit the surface. The image is reversed so things on the right side appear on the left. All the features on the object's surface can be seen in the image.

A

Read the statements below. Tick the boxes to say whether you think they are true or false.

1. Shadows are made by opaque objects.   True ☐   False ☐
2. Reflections are made when light is absent.   True ☐   False ☐
3. You can see lots of detail of the object in a shadow.   True ☐   False ☐
4. You can see lots of detail of the object in a reflection.   True ☐   False ☐
5. Another name for shadow is image.   True ☐   False ☐
6. When you wave your left hand in a mirror it looks like your right hand is waving.   True ☐   False ☐

7. Write your name on a piece of paper. Easy! Now place a mirror on the paper and look at the paper in the mirror. Try to write your name now. What happens?

167

Electrical components

Learning objective: To recognize the different components in an electrical circuit.

An electrical circuit is made up of components. Each one has a symbol.

Battery

A battery is also known as a cell. It provides the electricity for the circuit. The positive terminal of the battery must be connected to a negative terminal. If they are not connected in this way electricity will not flow in the circuit.

Wire

Wires conduct electricity between the different components of a circuit.

Lamp

The thin wire in the bulb releases light when electricity flows through it.

Switch

open   closed

When a switch is open electricity cannot flow. When it is closed electricity can flow round the circuit.

Motor

The motor produces a turning movement when electricity flows through it.

Buzzer

The buzzer makes a sound when electricity flows through it. The red wire must be connected to the positive terminal of a battery for the buzzer to work.

A Cover the top part of this page. Then, in the spaces below, draw a symbol for:

Motor   Battery   Buzzer   Lamp   Switch

Circuit diagrams

Learning objective: To relate the components of circuits to the symbols in the circuit.

Scientists use the symbols for electrical components to make circuit diagrams. These are accurate records of circuits, which are quick to make.

A diagram of a circuit with a switch, a battery and a lamp.

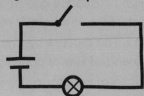

A diagram of a circuit with a switch, two batteries and a motor.

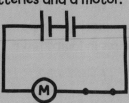

A

1. Have a go at drawing a circuit diagram for a circuit with two batteries, a switch and a buzzer in the space below.

2. Have a go at drawing a circuit diagram for a circuit with a battery, two lamps in a line and a switch in the space below.

Resistance

Learning objective: To know that electrical components resist the flow of electricity.

All electrical components, except batteries, have wire in them to allow electricity to flow through them. The wire offers some resistance to the electric current.

Wire thickness and resistance

A thick wire has a low resistance to an electric current and a thin wire has a high resistance. The wires used for connecting components have a low resistance but wires in lamps have a high resistance.

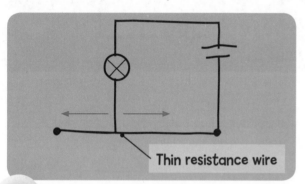

Thin resistance wire

Resistance and length

A long, thin wire made from a metal with a high resistance can be used to investigate how wire length affects resistance. The picture on the left shows the loose end of a wire connecting a short length of resistance wire into the circuit. The arrow shows how the loose end can be moved along the resistance wire to increase its length in the circuit. The lamp shines brightly when the resistance is low and dimly when it is high.

A

Look at the circuit diagram above and answer these questions.

1. Will the lamp shine brightly or dimly when a short length of resistance wire is used?

2. Will the lamp shine brightly or dimly when a long length of resistance wire is used?

3. How will the brightness of the bulb change when the loose end is moved to the right?

DEFINITION

resistance The property of a metal wire that slows down the flow of electricity through it.

Batteries and lamps

Learning objective: To know that the brightness of lamps can be changed.

Batteries supply electricity to circuits, and lamps offer resistance to current flow. The flow of electricity in a circuit is affected by changing the number of batteries or lamps in it.

> Two 1.5 volt batteries give a voltage of 3 volts.

Batteries and power
A battery's power to generate electricity is measured in volts (V). When batteries are added to a circuit their voltage combines to give greater power.

Lamps and resistance
The high resistance wire inside each lamp lights up when the current flows. If two lamps are joined in a row, or 'arranged in series', the resistance to the current doubles and both lamps shine less brightly. If two lamps are joined side by side, or 'arranged in parallel', the resistance of one does not add to the resistance of the other – both shine as brightly as though they were alone in the circuit.

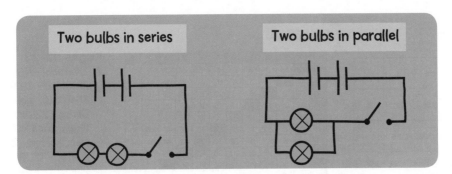

Two bulbs in series   Two bulbs in parallel

A

Have a go at answering these questions about resistance, batteries and lamps.

1. What is the voltage when three 1.5V batteries are put in a circuit?

2. What is the voltage in the circuit when two of the three batteries are taken out?

3. Two lamps are arranged in series in a circuit with one battery. Then a third lamp is added to the series. Do the lamps shine more brightly or more dimly?

Answers

Pages 10-11
A
1. 0.2
2. 0.35
3. 0.71
4. 0.96
5. 8.18
6. 8.4
7. 8.53
8. 8.79
9. 8.95
10. 16.18
11. 16.4
12. 16.53
13. 16.79
14. 16.99

B
Leatherback turtle	462.9kg
Green sea turtle	355.3kg
Loggerhead turtle	257.8kg
Flatback turtle	78.15kg
Hawksbill turtle	62.65kg
Kemp's Ridley turtle	60.45kg

C 2. 3.58, 3.85, 5.38, 5.83, 8.35, 8.53

Pages 12-13
A
1. 13.5
2. 96.7
3. 6.85
4. 33.46

B
1. 35 litres
2. 98.5km
3. 25kg

C
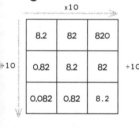

Pages 14-15
A
1. A triangular prism has 2 triangular faces and 3 rectangular faces.
2. A cube has 6 square faces.
3. A tetrahedron has 4 triangular faces.
4. A hexagonal prism has 2 hexagonal faces and 6 rectangular faces.
5. A square-based pyramid has 1 square face and 4 triangular faces.
6. A cuboid has 4 rectangular faces and 2 square faces.

B

	A	B	C	D	E	F	G	H
Prism	✔	✔	✔	✔	✔			✔
Pyramid						✔	✔	

Pages 16-17
A
1. 6
2. 16
3. 7
4. 18
5. 9
6. 12
7. 5
8. 6
9. 7
10. 63
11. 9
12. 6

B
1. 20
2. 5
3. 16
4. 11
5. 12
6. 5
7. 2
8. 47

C
1. 19 - (12 - 5) = 12
2. 16 - (10 - 6) = 12
3. 22 - (5 + 5) = 12
4. (6 + 13) - 7 = 12 or 6 + (13 - 7) = 12
5. (24 - 6) - 6 = 12
6. 20 - (10 - 2) = 12

D
1. 48
2. 7
3. 8
4. 21
5. 9
6. 20

Pages 18-19
A

	0	1	2	3	4	5	6	7	8	9	10
0	0	0	0	0	0	0	0	0	0	0	0
1	0	1	2	3	4	5	6	7	8	9	10
2	0	2	4	6	8	10	12	14	16	18	20
3	0	3	6	9	12	15	18	21	24	27	30
4	0	4	8	12	16	20	24	28	32	36	40
5	0	5	10	15	20	25	30	35	40	45	50
6	0	6	12	18	24	30	36	42	48	54	60
7	0	7	14	21	28	35	42	49	56	63	70
8	0	8	16	24	32	40	48	56	64	72	80
9	0	9	18	27	36	45	54	63	72	81	90
10	0	10	20	30	40	50	60	70	80	90	100

C
1. 24, 48
2. 15, 12
3. 46
4. 18, 77
5. 6, 50
6. 39, 92

D
1. 16
2. 49
3. 36
4. 81
5. 1
6. 4
7. 100
8. 9
9. 64
10. 25

Pages 20-21
A
1. (1, 8) (2, 4)
2. (1, 20) (2, 10) (4, 5)
3. (1, 24) (2, 12) (3, 8) (4, 6)
4. (1, 28) (2, 14) (4, 7)

(Multiples section)
B
1. 4, 8, 12, 16, 20, 24, 28, 32, 36, 40
2. 3, 6, 9, 12, 15, 18, 21, 24, 27, 30
3. 6, 12, 18, 24, 30, 36, 42, 48, 54, 60
4. 5, 10, 15, 20, 25, 30, 35, 40, 45, 50
5. 10, 20, 30, 40, 50, 60, 70, 80, 90, 100
6. 8, 16, 24, 32, 40, 48, 56, 64, 72, 80

C
1. 15, 30
2. 12, 24
3. 20, 40
4. 24, 48
5. 30, 60
6. 12, 24, 36

D
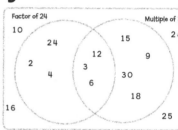

Pages 22-23
A
Liverpool - 469000
Bradford - 293700
Sheffield - 439900
Derby - 229400
Birmingham - 970900
Nottingham - 249600
Bristol - 420600
Plymouth - 243800

B
1. 800
2. 500
3. 100
4. 1200
5. 5900
6. 13700

C
1. 16kg
2. 21kg
3. 34kg
4. 45kg

D
1. 0.93
2. 7.08
3. 12.95
4. 7.59
5. 2.91
6. 30.08

Pages 24-25
A
1. 5.8cm
2. 1067cm
3. 9.1m
4. 135mm
5. 8300m
6. 9.4cm
7. 3.7km
8. 146mm

B
1. 35mm
2. 47mm
3. 26mm
4. 18mm
5. 62mm
6. 37mm

C 1. 96mm   2. 100mm
    3. 155mm   4. 90mm

Pages 26-27
A 1. 10:25   2. 09:55
    3. 19:00   4. 16:30
    5. 09:47   6. 17:25

B 1. 1.50pm   2. 11.08am
    3. 9.22am   4. 11.10pm
    5. 3.59pm   6. 9.34pm

C   Alarm wake up
    7.00am   07:00
    Meet for coffee
    10.00am   10:00
    Dentist
    11.35am   11:35
    Bus time
    2.18pm   14:18
    Taxi
    7.15pm   19:15
    Amazing Maths
    7.40pm   19:40

D   20:10 20.10.2010

Pages 28-29
A 1. 30%   5. 80%
    2. 20%   6. 10%
    3. 7%   7. 65%
    4. 22%   8. 12%

B 1. 5   4. 5
    2. 25   5. 34
    3. 5   6. 70

C 1. 1/4, 25%   4. 3/10, 30%
    2. 4/8, 50%   5. 2/5, 40%
    3. 7/10, 70%   6. 4/8, 50%

D 1. 1%
    2. 80%
    3. 80%
    4. 80%

Pages 30-31
A 1. 500g = 0.5kg
    2. 800g = 0.8kg
    3. 1400g = 1.4kg
    4. 1900g = 1.9kg
    5. 2000g = 2 kg

B 1. 2000ml = 2 litres
    2. 200ml = 0.2 litres
    3. 600ml = 0.6 litres
    4. 1100ml = 1.1 litres

C 1. 4 kg   5. 1 litre
    2. 2750g   6. 6500ml
    3. 5.5kg   7. 1.2 litres
    4. 3kg   8. 4000ml

Pages 32-33
A 1. 9468   4. 9563
    2. 7803   5. 7510
    3. 4479   6. 4020

B 1. 9625   4. 7869
    2. 9803   5. 7077
    3. 6078   6. 6435

C 1. 3420km   4. 4849km
    2. 5803km   5. 4490km
    3. 6281km

D

		4	6	**3**	8
+		9	1	6	3
1	**3**	**8**	**0**	**1**	

Pages 34-35
A 1. 3146   2. 5668
    3. 4370   4. 1273
    5. 4777   6. 4659

B 1. 7, 6, 0
    2. 9, 6, 5
    3. 9, 6, 1

C 1. 1161m
    2. 1381m
    3. 1279m
    4. Caribbean and Bering
    5. Caribbean
    6. Indian and Atlantic

Pages 36-37
A

Angle	1	2	3	4
Acute	✔			
Obtuse		✔		✔
Right-angled			✔	
Measured size (°)	60°	130°	90°	180°

B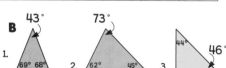

C

Pages 38-39
A 1. triangle   4. hexagon
    2. quadrilateral   5. heptagon
    3. pentagon   6. octagon

B 1. rectangle
    2. parallelogram
    3. trapezium
    4. square
    5. kite
    6. rhombus

C 1. always   4. never
    2. never   5. sometimes
    3. always   6. always

Page 40
A 1. rotated   2. reflected
    3. translated   4. reflected
    5. translated   6. rotated

Pages 42-43
A 1. 1444   2. 3108
    3. 456   4. 3286

B 1. 720 hours   4. 1800g
    2. 928km   5. 630m
    3. 700g   6. 735

C

Items	Amount in 1 pack	Number of packs	Total number of items
Pencils	28	76	2128
Chalk	15	33	495
Sharpeners	26	19	494
Erasers	48	14	672
Pens	52	58	3016
Crayons	34	47	1598

Pages 44-45
A 1. 162 r2   3. 47 r1
    2. 73 r2   4. 231 r2

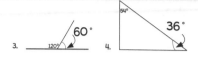

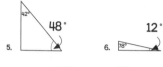

Answers

B

1 ——————▶ 271 ÷ 6
2 ——————▶ 608 ÷ 3
3 ——————▶ 315 ÷ 8
4 ——————▶ 454 ÷ 5
5 ——————▶ 149 ÷ 6
6 ——————▶ 398 ÷ 7
7 ——————▶ 259 ÷ 9
8 ——————▶ 458 ÷ 9
9 ——————▶ 259 ÷ 10

C

Day of the week	Eggs collected	Number of Full boxes (6 eggs)	Eggs left over
Monday	627	104	3
Tuesday	572	95	2
Wednesday	700	116	4
Thursday	644	107	2
Friday	683	113	5
Saturday	594	99	0
Sunday	735	122	3

Pages 46-47

A 1. 28cm² 3. 42cm²
2. 45cm² 4. 80cm²

B 1. 18cm² 3. 16cm²
2. 10cm² 4. 15cm²

C 1. 24cm² 4. 33cm²
2. 19cm² 5. 30cm²
3. 54cm² 6. 48cm²

Pages 48-49

A

1. $\frac{1}{3} = \frac{2}{6} = \frac{3}{9} = \frac{4}{12} = \frac{5}{15} = \frac{6}{18}$

2. $\frac{1}{4} = \frac{2}{8} = \frac{3}{12} = \frac{4}{16} = \frac{5}{20} = \frac{6}{24}$

3. $\frac{1}{2} = \frac{2}{4} = \frac{3}{6} = \frac{4}{8} = \frac{5}{10} = \frac{6}{12}$

4. $\frac{2}{3} = \frac{4}{6} = \frac{6}{9} = \frac{8}{12} = \frac{10}{15} = \frac{12}{18}$

B 1. > 5. >
2. < 6. >
3. < 7. <
4. < 8. >

C
$\frac{1}{10}$ ——▶ 0.1 $\frac{1}{5}$ ——▶ 0.2

$\frac{1}{4}$ ——▶ 0.25 $\frac{3}{10}$ ——▶ 0.3

$\frac{2}{5}$ ——▶ 0.4 $\frac{1}{2}$ ——▶ 0.5

$\frac{6}{10}$ ——▶ 0.6 and $\frac{3}{5}$ ——▶ 0.6

$\frac{7}{10}$ ——▶ 0.7 $\frac{3}{4}$ ——▶ 0.75

$\frac{4}{5}$ ——▶ 0.8 $\frac{9}{10}$ ——▶ 0.9

D

1. $\frac{1}{4}, \frac{3}{8}, \frac{1}{2}, \frac{10}{16}$

2. $\frac{1}{6}, \frac{1}{3}, \frac{6}{12}, \frac{3}{4}$

3. $\frac{5}{15}, \frac{1}{2}, \frac{3}{5}, \frac{2}{3}$

4. $\frac{4}{20}, \frac{1}{2}, \frac{7}{10}, \frac{4}{5}$

Pages 50-51

A 1. $\frac{2}{5}$ 2. $\frac{1}{10}$ 3. $\frac{1}{2}$

4. $\frac{4}{5}$ 5. $\frac{1}{4}$ 6. $\frac{3}{4}$

B 1. 70% 4. 84%
2. 90% 5. 76%
3. 80%

C 1. 7cm 5. 35ml
2. 27km 6. 20m
3. 4 litres 7. 60g
4. 12kg 8. 200mm

D

	50%	25%	10%	40%	5%
60m	30m	15m	6m	24m	3m
50m	25m	12.5m	5m	20m	2.5m
300m	150m	75m	30m	120m	15m
250m	125m	62.5m	25m	100m	12.5m

Pages 52-53

A 1. 67.83 3. 91.81
2. 84.76 4. 85.51

B 1. 43.02 3. 37.76
2. 47.23 4. 41.78

C 1. 26.63 l 3. 68.01kg
2. 63.91m 4. 81.23kg

D 1. 0.76 4. 0.09
2. 0.51 5. 1.34
3. Eileen and Nikki

Pages 54-55

A 1. 3 5. 19
2. 15 6. 8
3. 5 7. 4
4. 8 8. 9

B 1. 9 5. 8
2. 4 6. 5
3. 7 7. 20
4. 6 8. 5

C 1. 4 4. 9
2. 6 5. 3
3. 7 6. 10

D 1. 10t
2. 12y
3. 25 - n

Pages 56-57

A 1. (3, 5)
2. (8, 8)

B 1. Triangle B
(4, 1) (6, 4) (7, 1)
2. Triangle C
(0, 3) (3, 2) (3, 6)
Triangle D
(5, 2) (5, 6) (8, 3)
3. Triangle E
(0, 5) (4, 5) (4, 8)
Triangle F
(4, 2) (4, 5) (8, 5)

Pages 58-59

A 1. 4/mode
2. 4/median

B 1. 140cm 4. 1
2. 140cm 5. Amy
3. 150cm 6. 145cm

C median 10cm
mode 10cm
mean 10cm
Challenge
median 2 hours
mode 2 hours
mean 3 hours

Pages 60-61

A 1. There is an evens chance of
picking a multiple of 2.

2. There is a certain chance of picking a diamond.

3. There is a poor chance of picking a multiple of 5.

4. There is a poor chance of picking a number over 6.

5. It is impossible to pick the queen of diamonds.

6. There is a poor chance of picking the 9 of diamonds.

B 1. $\dfrac{1}{2}$ 2. $\dfrac{1}{10}$

3. $\dfrac{3}{10}$ 4. $\dfrac{4}{10}$ or $\dfrac{2}{5}$

5. $\dfrac{9}{10}$ 6. $\dfrac{1}{10}$

C 1. 1 in 6 2. 1 in 2
3. 1 in 3 4. 1 in 3
5. 1 in 2 6. 1 in 6

D 1. 12 red 2. 6 green
3. 4 blue 4. 2 black
5. 0 yellow

Pages 62-63

A
1. $\dfrac{1}{3}$ 2. $\dfrac{1}{4}$

3. $\dfrac{1}{2}$ 4. $\dfrac{2}{3}$

5. $\dfrac{2}{5}$ 6. $\dfrac{3}{4}$

B
1.

Pineapples	Oranges	Total
1	4	5
2	8	10
5	20	25
8	32	40
10	40	50

2.

Bananas	Peaches	Total
2	3	5
4	6	10
12	18	30
16	24	40
20	30	50

C 1. butter 150g flour 200g
carrots 100g sugar 60g
eggs 50g walnuts 40g
2. flour 180g butter 90g
sugar 60g choc chips 30g

D
butter 300g flour 400g
carrots 200g sugar 120g
eggs 100g walnuts 80g

Page 65

A caterpillar: cat, pillar, pill, ate, ill
television: vision, is, on
cupboard: cup, board, boar, oar
wardrobe: ward, robe, rob, war
supermarket: super, market, mark
subway: way, sub
basketball: basket, ball, ask. all
crossword: cross, word, or

B On Saturday, we took the train into town. We usually go by car because Mum says the train fare is too dear, but she agrees it's much faster by train. We even had a drink on the train, which we can't do in the car! We didn't need to pay for parking either so I think the train was cheaper in the end!

Pages 66-67

A 1. bananas
girls
boys
days
stars

2. potatoes
buses
boxes
dishes
watches
dresses
tomatoes
brushes
benches
glasses
wishes
volcanoes

B 1. leaves
knives
calves
2. babies
butterflies
ponies
stories
parties
ladies
3. geese
sheep
deer
feet
children
women

Pages 68-69

A 1. autograph
telescope
automatic
automobile
telephone
autobiography
2. anti-ageing =
not ageing or stops ageing
anti-bacterial =
not bacterial or stops bacteria
anti-freeze = stops freezing

B Toothpaste would have an anti-bacterial.

175

Answers

C magician: someone who performs magic tricks.
pianist: someone who plays the piano.
chemist: someone who works with chemicals.
beautician: someone who works in beauty.
electrician: someone who works with electricity.
musician: someone who plays a musical instrument.
politician: someone works in politics.
biologist: someone who works in biology.

D singer, gardener, teacher, climber, walker, player.

Pages 70-71

A When Superboy whispered a secret word, his school jumper became a long, shiny, red cloak and his spectacles morphed into a mirrored, black mask. His super-human powers enabled him to climb vertical walls, scale rooftops, sense danger and bring wrong-doers to justice.

B All of a sudden, the rock door split open and a dark figure sprang out! It was the Evil Weevil, Superboy's deadliest enemy. Weevil eyed him menacingly for a second and lunged forward with a blood curdling battle cry!

C How was Superboy going to defeat the Evil Weevil? Was he cunning and clever enough to outwit him? Everyone knew that the Weevil was a wimp really but he was a scary wimp, all the same. What would happen if Superboy failed? Would the Earth be plunged into another inter-planetary war?

D "So, Superboy, we meet at last," the Weevil sneered. "It's a shame we don't have time to strike up a friendship! Ha, ha, ha!" The Weevil laughed at his own feeble joke.
"I wouldn't worry, Weevil," replied Superboy. "You'll have plenty of time to make friends with the cockroaches you'll meet in the state planetary prison!"

Pages 72-73

A 1. I can't find it. It's gone!
2. That's my friend's house.
3. It's Toni's book.
4. Where's Mrs Dale's class?
5. They'll be late for school.
6. We're going to Gina's party.

B can't: cannot; it's: it is, that's: that is; they'll: they will, where's: where is; we're: we are

C 1. The clown's car fell apart.
2. The clowns' car fell apart.
3. The dog's owner went to the Pooch Parlour.
4. The dogs' owner went to the Pooch Parlour.
5. The girl's rabbit ran away.
6. The girls' rabbit ran away.
7. The man's sunglasses were expensive.
8. The men's sunglasses were expensive.

Pages 74-75

A 1. It was lucky for me that it was not going to be a problem.
2. The sun was burning hot so we had to put on lashings of sunscreen.
3. She clicked her fingers and the little dog began to dance.

B First, we went to the Tower of London to see the Crown Jewels. Next, we saw Big Ben and, after lunch, we had a great time at the London Dungeon. Although it rained for most of the day we didn't really notice, except when we finally got back to the bus station and had to wait ages for the bus to come... in the rain!

C First, we went on the Ghost Train. It wasn't as scary as we thought it was going to be. But then we went on the Rocky Coaster and that was terrifying! We thought we were going to go flying off the track! Next, we got a real soaking on the Log Flume and the Crazy Rapids. Lastly, we had a ride on the Angry Camel and it was so funny that we couldn't stop laughing.

Pages 76-77

A 1. Mr Parker gave Class 5 a detention so they missed their playtime.
2. Our class won the merit prize so we are going on a trip to the zoo.
3. Chris is team captain because he is the best at football.
4. Katie loves swimming so she joined the swimming club.
5. I usually like history but today it was boring.
6. We watched a film about spiders because we were doing a topic on them.

B 1. It's mine. 2. This is yours. 3. The coats are theirs. 4. The cat is hers. 5. The dog eats its dinner.

Pages 78-79

A I drew, I wrote, I swam, I caught, I saw, I went, I ate.

C You could have:
1. The giant stomped angrily across the room.
2. "Hubble, bubble, toil and trouble," cackled the witch menacingly.
3. The elf sneaked quietly into the shop.
4. The vampire suddenly leaped out of the coffin.
5. The wizard carefully concocted a potion.
6. The boy quickly snatched the wand.

Page 81

B 1. Joe's a sly fox! Joe might have done something behind someone's back.
2. Jen's a rock. Jen is loyal and someone you can depend on.

D 1. As hard as nails.
2. As strong as an ox.
3. As weak as a kitten.
4. As white as a sheet.
5. As cold as ice.
6. As red as a beetroot.

Pages 82-83

A 1. Things become easier with practice.
2. Fix something now before it gets worse.
3. Think before you act.
4. Don't question generosity.
5. Don't assign too many people to one job.

B 1. Give it your best performance.
2. To get caught out.
3. It's raining heavily.
4. Things are going well.

C 1. The balloon burst with a loud pop.
2. The glass smashed onto the floor.
3. My feet squelched in thick mud.
4. The heavy door closed with a thud.
5. The bees buzzed around the flowers.
6. The waves crashed onto the rocks.
7. The drink fizzed in the can.

D 1. gaggle of geese
2. pack of wolves
3. pride of lions
4. herd of cows
5. flock of birds
6. swarm of bees
7. school of dolphins

Page 85

A 1. 2nd, 2. 3rd, 3. 1st

Page 87

A 1. He/she was less afraid of the captain than everyone else.
2. He was a scary and angry man who, when he drank too much, would often fly into a rage.
3. He would "sit and sing his wicked, old, sea-songs" and tell stories.
4. They were afraid that if they didn't sing loudly he would notice them and might kill them.
5. He would get angry when they asked questions or, sometimes, when they didn't ask questions, because he thought they weren't listening.
6. He would slap his hand on the table when he wanted silence.
7. The person telling the story is someone who knew the captain well and had seen him at the inn many times.

Page 89

A 1. goeth, seizeth, doth, 'tis.
2. The poet's name is John Bunyan.
3. He died in 1688.
4. Any of these pairs rhyme: sure/endure; on/upon; go/so; sure/procure.
5. The snail eats flowers and herbs.
6. Others couldn't find food to satisfy them.
7. She knows what her goal is and achieves it.

Pages 90-91

A The missing letter in each word is 's'.

B Rhymes: hands/lands/stands; crawls/walls/falls.
Alliterations: clasps/crag/crooked/close; lonely/lands; watches/walls.

Page 93

A "Greetings, Sir, on this the three hundred and sixty-sixth day of term!" exclaimed Bot brightly, as he entered the date on the touch-screen learning wall.

"Give out the books please, Bot," said 1471.

"Do you mean those curious, pre-computer-age page-turners, Sir? We haven't used those for over a thousand years!" said Bot.

"I know we haven't, but I thought we'd start with an ancient history lesson today!" replied 1471.

Answers

Page 95

A 1. They were at war because the Greek queen, Helen, had been abducted by Paris, the Trojan prince.

2. Odysseus was a Greek.

3. They believed the war was over because they saw the Greek ships sailing away.

4. He was very important because he persuaded them that the horse was lucky.

5. They were happy that the war was over.

6. Yes, Odysseus' trick worked because the Greeks rescued Helen and destroyed Troy.

Page 97

A 1. One of the biggest species of jellyfish is found in the Antarctic Sea.

2. One of the deadliest jellyfish is the Box Jelly.

3. Jellyfish eat shrimp, plankton and microscopic fish, or even other jellyfish.

4. Jellyfish are prey to creatures that don't fear their tentacles, eg turtles or other jellyfish.

Pages 100-101

A These words were misspelt: was, father, able, married, writer.

B 1. He was 78 years old when he died.

2. Dates are important in a biography because they help us to structure our writing and to better understand events in people's lives.

3. 1812: Charles Dickens was born in 1812.

1824: His father was sent to prison in 1824.

1829: He began his career as a journalist in 1829.

1836: He got married in 1836.

1890: He died in 1890.

Page 103

A 1. Inedible means not good enough to eat.

2. Although we had a wonderful view of the rubbish bins.

3. Firstly, secondly, thirdly, finally.

4. A 'cupboard' is a metaphor for the room they stayed in.

5. It would have been difficult for him to stop the cicadas!

6. The address states Naples, Italy.

Pages 106-107

A Cinderella 4
Snow White 2
Mr Bean's Holiday 5
The Lord of the Rings 1
Around the World in 80 Days 3

B Cinderella: she wanted to go to the ball.

Puss in Boots: he was just a cat, but he wanted to be important.

Spiderman: he wanted to rid the world of evil.

Buzz Lightyear: he wanted to be a favourite toy.

Nemo: he wanted to find his way back home.

Page 108

A 1. fairytale castle or forest – Fairy Stories

2. school or home – Modern stories

3. old house or graveyard at night – Spooky stories

4. remote or faraway place – Adventure stories

5. other planets – Science fiction stories

B When: in summer. Where: on the beach.

The summer sun is high in the sky. The crashing waves break against my chest as I race towards them with my board. In front of me, I hear my friends shouting and I taste excitement in the salty air.

Page 111

B Possible answers:

My cheeks feel their icy breath.
Now arrows are falling like rain.
Towards the enemy they fly.
In his direction the arrows flew.
One has hit him in the eye.
As I watch Harold die.
It's a tragedy, but the war is won.

Page 116

A Our Super Sandwiches are made with...

1. special care.

2. best local ingredients.

3. 10 tasty fillings.

Page 120

A The heart pumps the blood into the arteries and it travels to all parts of the body. The blood returns to the heart in blood vessels called veins.

Page 121

A 65 person lying down, 70 person standing, 90 person walking, 120 person running.

Page 122
A People who are ill take medicines to get better. The medicines can contain drugs to help them recover. Harmful drugs like cocaine make people become addicts. Addicts are in danger of being killed by the drugs they take.

Page 123
A The poster could show healthy people not smoking or drinking too much alcohol and ill-looking people who do. The children could also use sources such as advertisements in magazines to help them with their ideas.

Page 124
A

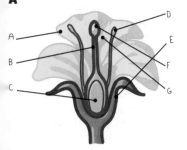

Page 125
A

	Insect-pollinated flower	Wind-pollinated flower
Large petals	✓	
Strong scent	✓	
Nectar	✓	
Little pollen	✓	
Lots of pollen		✓
Smooth pollen		✓
Spiky pollen	✓	

Page 126
A Stigma makes pollen grains stick.

Pollen grain carries a substance from a flower for fertilization. Pollen tube carries a substance from a pollen grain to an ovule.

Page 127
B 1-Seed germinates.
2-Seedling starts to grow.
3-Plant fully grown.
4-Plant makes flowers.
5-Flowers makes fruits.
6-Plant disperses fruit.

Page 128
A You have increased in size and your head has got smaller in proportion to your body. The colour of your hair may have changed.

Page 129
A A frog's egg is surrounded by jelly. A tadpole hatches from the egg. It has a long tail and looks like a little fish. In time the tadpole grows legs and a big head and its tail disappears. When this happens it has turned into a frog.

Page 130
A 40 cm^3

Page 131
A Helium - lighter than air.
Natural gas - used in some cookers.

Carbon dioxide - used to make food by plants

Page 132
A A piece of chocolate was left on a sunny windowsill. As it got warmer its firm sides started to sag and it began to lose its shape. When the temperature reached melting point the chocolate turned into a liquid and dropped off the windowsill.

Page 133
A

Substance	Freezing point (°C)	
Beeswax	64°C	2
Water	0°C	5
Chocolate	25°C	4
Lard	43°C	3
Pewter	240°C	1

3 would freeze.

Page 134
A Hot, dry, windy air.

Page 135
A

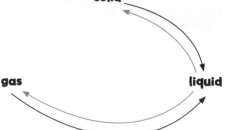

Page 136
A Earth 12,756 km.
Moon 3476 km.
Sun 1,392,000 km.
The Moon is nearer the Earth than the Sun.

Answers

Page 137
A The answers to 1 and 2 will depend on the time of year now. 3 will depend on the month in which the birthday takes place.

Page 138
A Anti-clockwise. C, A, B.

Page 139
A 1. False,
2. True,
3. False,
4. True,
5. False,
6. True.

Page 140
A 1. Waxing 1 2 3.
2. Waning 5 6 7.

Page 141
A Pluto, Neptune, Uranus, Saturn, Jupiter, Asteroid belt, Mars, Earth, Venus, Mercury, Mercury, Venus, Earth, Mars, Asteroid belt, Jupiter, Saturn, Uranus, Neptune, Pluto.

Page 142
A Sound travels fastest through solids. Sound travels slowest through gases.

Page 143
A 1. By wrapping the same thickness of material around the sound source.
2. B was the best insulator.

Page 144
Professor's question - A long piece of vibrating ruler has a lower pitch than a shorter piece.
A 2. Bottom C note on piano.
3. Thunder.
4. Ordinary voice.

5. Baby's first cry.
6. Chainsaw.
7. Top note on piano.

Page 145
A 1. Drum B has the lower pitch.
2. String B has the higher pitch.
3. It makes the pitch lower.

Page 146
A When light shines on a leaf it provides energy for water and carbon dioxide to be changed into food and oxygen.
The oxygen made by plants is used by animals when they breathe in. (Some is also used by plants).
The carbon dioxide for the plant to use is breathed out by animals. (Plants also make some, and carbon dioxide is also made when things burn.)

Page 147
A 1. A tap root is thicker with fewer side roots, which spread out in the soil. It goes deeper into the soil.
2. Gravelly soil drains best. (A) Clay soil has the worst drainage. (C)

Page 148
A 1. Beetle and deer are using the plants for shelter
2. A deer is using a plant as food.
3. A spider is using the plant to set a trap.

Page 149
A The animals are
A millipede,
B earthworm,
C insect,
D snail,
E harvestman,

F slug,
G woodlouse,
H spider,
I centipede.

Page 150
A stiff tail feathers, chisel-shaped beak, two toes pointing backwards instead of one, strong claws, strong skull, long tongue.

Page 151
A

seed ⇒ beetle ⇒ shrew ⇒ owl ⇒

Page 152
A 1. A virus might give you a cold.
2. Bacteria are removed when you brush your teeth.
3. Bacteria and fungi might grow on an orange.
4. Bacteria and fungi make the contents of a compost bin rot.

Page 153
A The bread would not have bubbles in it or have a spongy texture. The yeast needs the sugar to feed on and make bubbles.

Page 154
A 1. Sand, flour and custard powder can be separated from the water by filtering.
2. A filter has holes in it that are large enough to let a liquid through, but are too small to let particles of undissolved solid through.

Page 155
A When salt is mixed with water it dissolves and makes a solution.

If the solution is boiled the water turns to steam and leaves the salt behind. The steam can be turned to water again by cooling it down in a process called condensation.

Page 156
A All of the statements are correct.

Page 157
A 1. 40 seconds.
2. 40 seconds.
3. 20 degrees Celsius.

Page 158
A 1 baking powder.
2 flour.
3 plaster of Paris.

Page 159
A 1. water vapour (gas) and carbon dioxide (gas).
2.

Process	Reversible	Irreversible
Melting of wax	✓	
Burning of wood		✓
Baking bread		✓
Freezing water	✓	
Mixing flour and water		✓

Page 160
A 1. The force of gravity pulls them down towards the centre of the Earth.
2. 110 Newtons.
3. 60 Newtons.

Page 161
A 1. How the length of the elastic band extends as weights are attached to it.
2. 6mm.
3 12 Newtons.
4. The elastic band broke.

Page 162
A 1. 1, 3 ,4 and 6 floated.
2. It would sink.

Page 163
A 1.

Spinner wing length (cm)	Trial 1 fall (secs)	Trial 2 fall (secs)	Trial 3 fall (secs)	Trial 4 fall (secs)	Trial 5 fall (secs)	Average fall (secs)
3	2	3	4	2	4	3
6	4	5	6	5	5	5
10	7	8	6	8	6	7

2. The larger the wing the slower the fall.
3. The larger wings have a larger air resistance, which slows down the fall.

Page 164
A An arrow should go from the torch to the book. A second arrow should go from the book to the eye.

Page 165
A 1.

Angle of incident ray	Angle of reflected ray
20	20
30	30
63	63
77	77

2. The angles are always the same. The light leaves the mirror at the same angle at which it struck it.

Page 166
A 1. It becomes larger.
2. Moving the torch nearer object, screen moved away from object, object moved away from screen.

Page 167
A 1. True.
2. False.
3. False.
4. True.
5. False.

6. True.
7. You should find that writing your name is much more difficult to do as the image you are looking at is a reverse of the real view of the paper.

Page 168
A Symbol for a:

Motor

battery

buzzer

switch

lamp

Page 169
A 1.

2.

Page 170
A 1. Brightly.
2. Dimly.
3. From dim to bright.

Page 171
A 1. 4.5 V.
2. 1.5 V.
3. More dimly.

Notes

Notes

Notes

Notes

Index

Index